FEATHERING YOUR NEST

An Interactive Workbook and Guide to a Loving Lesbian Relationship

Gwen Leonhard, M.Ed.
& Jennie Mast, MSW, BCSW

RISING TIDE PRESS

1997

Rising Tide Press
5 Kivy Street
Huntington Station, NY 11746
(516) 427-1289

Printed in the United States on acid-free paper.

Publisher's note:
All characters, places and situations in this book are fictitious and any resemblance to persons (living or dead) is purely coincidental.

Publisher's Acknowledgments:
The publisher is grateful for all the support and expertise offered by the members of its editorial board: Bobbi Bauer, Beth Heyn, Hat Edwards, Pat G. and Candy T. Special thanks to Edna G. for believing in us, and to the feminist and gay bookstores for being there.

First printing January 1997
10 9 8 7 6 5 4 3 2 1

Edited by Lee Boojamra and Alice Frier
Book cover art: Karen Ramsey

Leonhard, Gwen 1953-
        Feathering Your Nest/Gwen Leonhard and Jennie Mast
                p.cm
ISBN 1-883061-13-X
Library of Congress Catalog Card Number 96-67601

FEATHERING YOUR NEST

An Interactive Workbook
and Guide to a
Loving Lesbian Relationship

**Gwen Leonhard, M.Ed.
& Jennie Mast, MSW, BCSW**

Acknowledgments

Special Thanks to:

Kim Fernandez Leonhard,
for being the love of Gwen's life,
the one she adores

Mary Lasseigne,
for her love and devotion to Jennie

Our Parents,
for raising loving and strong daughters

Lee Boojamra and Alice Frier
at Rising Tide Press,
for believing in the concept

Ben Meroney,
for his legal assistance and generosity

Richard Leonhard and Nicole and Don Tussel,
for their secretarial and computer skills

Winnie Hough
Judy Orr
Jennifer Nolan

All of the wonderful women who have participated in
The Positive Living Alliance

Come and fly with me
  to a safe place,
  our gentle hideaway,
Where we are sheltered
  from the storm;
Soar with me
  wing to wing
  beyond the haven here
Or climb
  through the sky alone
  holding my favor near.
Know always
  that your home is here
  with me, my friend,
To nestle and dream
  in our delight.
Bring to me your fears
  and hopes
And trust in what we have.
There's sweet love and care
  that we share best
In the feathering of our nest.

—G.L.

Table of Contents

FOREWORD

Keeping a relationship both healthy and exciting can be a very difficult task. From my own experiences and by witnessing friends begin and end many relationships, I have often wondered what attributes keep some couples together for many years, while others go from one relationship to another after a relatively short time. Through my work as a social worker and through my own experiences in life, I now know that successful relationships take a tremendous amount of effort and devotion. You cannot just sit back and expect your relationship to flow in everlasting harmony. It requires a serious commitment.

Feathering Your Nest is designed to assist lesbian couples who want a long-lasting, happy and secure relationship. There are many exercises for you and your partner to do together, along with various ideas to assist you in living a more fulfilling life within your relationship. This book is long overdue, and I only wish that I had had such a wonderful tool years ago. It probably would have saved me from more than just a couple of heartaches. When my lover and I completed the exercises in this book, we were surprised that in spite of our having lived together for years, we actually learned so much more about each other and our relationship. More than anything, the book stimulated discussion about feeling, desires, perspective and direction. We hope it does the same for you.

For many individuals, self-help books are addictive but, ultimately, useless. It's like trying to lose weight by simply reading a diet book. It is important for you to *be active* in order to make things happen and to bring about change. That is why it is crucial for you to do the exercises as you are reading *Feathering Your Nest*. Have fun while you are doing them, but also take the exercises seriously and work towards incorporating the concepts into your relationship. This is not a book to be read once and put away to collect dust. Keep this book handy on your active bookshelf — somewhere within reach — and refer to it periodically, reworking the exercises if need be.

Gwen and I have been actively working for the Positive Living Alliance (PLA) for some time to assist lesbian and gay couples in attaining healthier and happier relationships. This work, and our combined theoretical backgrounds in psychology and education, have happily resulted in *Feathering Your Nest*. We hope it brings you insight and a renewed excitement about your relationship.

Go ahead. Get started on your journey through the book and through your lives together.

——Jennie Mast, MSW, BSW

INTRODUCTION:

KNOWING IT CAN WORK

We lesbians are not all alike. We come from different backgrounds and we face distinct futures separate from one another. We do, however, face many of the same joys and many of the same problems. Although *Feathering Your Nest* will examine some of the unique obstacles that face lesbian couples, its primary focus will be on the possibility of achieving a healthy and happy lesbian relationship. It is our hope that you will draw an abundance of information from the book and from within yourself.

FEELING GOOD ABOUT WHO YOU ARE

Like heterosexual couples, lesbian and gay couples are faced with typical relationship pressures from sources such as in-laws, finances, holiday expectations and career moves. But in addition, we alone are faced with a more sinister burden — homophobia. It shouldn't come as a big surprise that although the lesbian and gay community has made much progress, we still live in a predominantly homophobic world. For anyone who is unaware of what homophobia is, it is an abnormal fear of homosexuals and lesbians. It often results in inaccurate stereotypes, avoidance, societal and religious condemnation, and hostility. Homohatred, which in its severest form has taken a significant toll on the lives of many lesbians and especially gay men, is one of the reactions to that abnormal fear. We have all seen it in one form or another and have recognized it when it has come our way from heterosexual society.

It Is Important to Feel Good About Being a Lesbian In Order To Have a Have a Healthy Lesbian Relationship

In their article "An Introduction to Therapy Issues of Lesbian and Gay Male Couples," Laura S. Brown, Ph.D., and Don Zimmer, M.Ed., examine another side of the homophobia issue. Are we aware of the possibility that some of the fear and hatred that we face comes from **within** ourselves? Homophobic programming has infiltrated most of our lives since we were babies. Most of us, for example, have grown up with exposure to negative feelings about "dykes" and "queers."

We've been taught — sometimes in very subtle ways, sometimes in very blatant and harsh ways — to dislike and make fun of these "perverted" people. Think about it. Have you ever disliked or made fun of one of those "dykes" or "queers" for being who she/he is? Do you think that your own mild brand of homophobia plays a part in your intimate relationships? Do you feel guilty about having lesbian sex? It would be a monumental struggle to feel good about yourself or about your lover if you feel bad about something as important as your sexuality. Positive self-esteem, which includes how you see yourself sexually, is a key ingredient to a healthy and happy relationship. There's not much you can do about the rampant external homophobia that spans the globe; but, if you do have feelings of internal homophobia, there is definitely something you can do. Consider seeking the counsel of a reputable lesbian-friendly psychologist or social worker to help eradicate the negative internal feelings that are keeping you from developing into the best woman you can be and from building a healthy nest with the woman you love.

TAKE OFF YOUR COAT And STAY AWHILE

After interviewing lesbians throughout the United States, researchers discovered a pattern that many of us have followed. We have often started our journey through relationships bouncing from one lover to the next, making and breaking "commitments" along the way. We didn't take the time to really get to know the other person, partially because we really didn't know ourselves. Our "commitments" were often made in order to "lay claim" to the woman we wanted with us. The "commitment" was, in fact, our semi-sure way of ensuring that our partner would not stray. Women excited us, and we thrived on the thrill of having new women lavish their affections upon us. We relished the exhilaration of the new, the unknown, the tumultuous. "Commitments" that we made to one woman were frequently meaningless when a new one entered the scene, or when compromise was needed. At the same time, we often became involved and "fell in love" with the "wrong" women. Not that they weren't wonderful; they were just not women who were in a position to make a serious commitment to us. Similarly, we were often not in a position to make one to them. We were too egotistical and curious. Dead-end, superficial relationships that were exciting and passionate, but often painful and frustrating, took the place of serious commitments. But the choices were ours and there was nothing coincidental about them. And despite the intense emotions we felt while involved in the various relationships, somehow they never led to long-term happy and healthy unions. Maybe we didn't even think that kind of union was an option. Although some of our parents had great long-term marriages, we didn't have a clue about how to develop the same type of relationship with a woman. We certainly didn't have the role models or the encouragement that straight couples have had. Perhaps we didn't think we, as lesbians, had the right to develop a healthy relationship.

Many couples — straight, gay, and lesbian — get caught up in an all-too-familiar cycle. See if you recognize yourself or a friend in this scenario. As a lesbian, you go out on a date with a woman for the first time. You're smitten. The entire next day, you just can't stop talking or thinking about her. She's just the person you want in your life. So you go out on a second date with her and the two of you have a wild night of sex. You stay home together on the third date, and you tell her that you've never met anyone quite like her. You stare into each other's eyes and express your heartfelt love for one another. You feel the magic. On the fourth date, you set up house together. For the first two years, the honeymoon is definitely on and there is no doubt in either one's mind that it will last forever. Near the start of the third year, things get a bit dull. She's not so exciting or even interesting; in fact, you wonder if she ever was. By the middle of the third year, you're keeping your eyes open for the woman who will take your present mate's place. After all, you don't want to leave one relationship before you have another one lined up. By the beginning of the fourth year, you've packed your bags and moved out of the first relationship. You and your new love move in together. The cycle begins again. Although the description here sounds a bit exaggerated, it's likely that you've seen a friend or a family member or someone else get caught up in a similar cycle.

Psychological research has shown that most lesbians and gays enter into relationships actually expecting them to be short and void of any *real* commitment. We've been taught by much of the straight world that our relationships are meaningless at best, evil at worst. Have some of their teachings sunk in? Because same-sex couples often believe that they will eventually break up with their lovers, many don't make serious commitments in the first place. When the proverbial waters of the relationship get choppy, one or the other partner jumps ship and swims away. There is often no real investment into the relationship. There's often no real sense of "'til death do us part." Because many same-sex couples believe that their relationships won't last, their thoughts become self-fulfilling prophecies. Perhaps being aware of the faulty lessons taught to us by the mostly heterosexual world is the first step in helping us overcome the problems we now face in our lives. Being the lovable women that we are, we don't deserve the fear or hatred that has come our way. Being the strong women that we are, we can withstand the inevitable hard times that occur in all relationships and know that we can get through them together in order to attain healthy and happy long-term relationships.

It is easy for lesbians to see themselves as being "single," especially since we are presently denied the legal status that "binds" heterosexuals together in marriage. (This is not to say that all heterosexual marriages stay together because of that legal status.) Many lesbians find it easier to just leave the current relationship when problems arise or when they get a bit bored. The idea that a successful relationship involves work doesn't appeal to us since there's often another woman waiting in the wings.

The same is often true of heterosexuals; it's just sometimes a bit more complicated for them to split up because of the legal rigmarole, church teachings, and family pressure pushing them to work at their "sanctified" unions. After all, can you picture the parents of most lesbians telling their daughters to seek counseling in order to stay together with Melody or Susan or Linda? It's not likely in most cases. Many parents, in fact, might be thinking, "Okay, now that *this* relationship is over, she just might find the right man." Since there are usually no children or tangled financial matters to stand in the way, it's pretty easy to just end the relationship and move on. Now you may be thinking, "There's a positive side to that conclusion." Perhaps, but there are probably many lesbian couples who would still be together if they had only hurdled the inevitable obstacles and creatively worked at making their relationship more exciting and loving. *Feathering Your Nest* will provide you with suggestions for surmounting some of the obstacles so you can make your relationship more exciting, loving and durable. It's up to you to decide whether this is the kind of relationship you want for yourself.

WHERE'S THE FIRE?

According to therapist James K. Whittaker's article "Models of Group Development," healthy relationships progress through certain phases. Because each phase supplies you with valuable tools to eventually attain a successful union, it's important not to race through them. Take it slow and easy. Learning this lesson just could be the key to achieving a successful long-term lesbian relationship.

RELATIONSHIP STAGES

During Phase 1 of relationship development, you start dating and getting to know one another. You discover delightful similarities that bind you. You also discover differences — some that you like, some that you don't. You can be sure that not all of the important differences will pop to the surface in the initial stages of a relationship; after all, it is in the early stages where we are doing our utmost to endear ourselves to each other. Although there can be much excitement and eager curiosity during Phase 1, there is no authentic commitment and there is no real trust. The uncertainty of your role in her life and hers in yours is the source of much of that early "passion." You don't really know what to expect from the new person in your life. During this phase, it is best for you to still be spending time with other women.

In Phase 2 of relationship development, you make the decision about whether you want to continue seeing one another; it's definitely not where you decide to spend eternity together. After you have dated for a while and you have decided that you do want to see more of each other, you'll go through a phase of conflict where your first real argument occurs. Power struggles — some extremely subtle, some more overt — will ensue. You're both fighting for a position in the relationship. How do you fit into each other's lives? Is one of you more dominant than the other? What can you expect from one another? Are you where you want to be on her priority list? With certain problem-solving skills and a bit of patience, the two of you can pull through Phase 2 with a clearer understanding of who each of you is in the new shape of each other's lives. If the problems are resolved, you can then move forward to the next phase of the relationship. If the problems are not fully resolved, count on them continually popping up throughout the rest of your time together in either a recognizable form or disguised as something new.

Phase 3 of relationship development is one of true intimacy and conscious commitment to a future together. This is when you develop a feeling of "us" instead of "me." It's the phase when you've made a deliberate — not lustful — decision to love one another. With proper handling of the tools you have developed during each phase of the relationship, the likelihood of functioning as a healthy couple and of maturely solving conflicts will be increased. During Phases 1 and 2, the couple might test branches for a possible nesting site. They might discuss what materials they will use to construct their future nest. It is only in the final phase, however, that you can truly begin feathering the nest both of you have consciously decided to build together.

It is important to give yourself time to go through the natural phases of getting to know the other person. Relationships develop best when they are based on a commitment to build together, not to escape loneliness. You have to do more than *want* the relationship to succeed; you have to work at making it succeed. Making the commitment work is not a job for wimps! Did you notice that the words "job" and "work" were used in that last sentence? That's right. It is a job; and, hopefully, the relationship will be a job you will cherish and anticipate joyously each day. A successful relationship requires couples to work at their union together with devotion and care. Once again, you've got to work at it beyond the excitement of the beginning of a relationship. *The beginning doesn't last; the beginning is just the beginning!*

WHAT'S A WOMAN TO DO?

Throughout the workbook we invite you to do the exercises and participate in the suggested activities. Some of the exercises are designed for you to answer separately from your lover; others are meant for you and your lover to answer together. Some are designed for you to write down a response; others are meant for you to discuss with your partner. The effectiveness of *Feathering Your Nest* is based on how honestly you approach the questions and your joint discussions of the issues presented.

Notice as you move through *Feathering Your Nest* how material from one chapter continually overlaps material from the others. So it is with relationships. There is no easy way to separate one component from the others, since every aspect is enmeshed with every other aspect. It's difficult, for example, to discuss ideas in the chapter "Create Fun and Excitement" without touching upon some of the ideas in the chapter "Generate Goals and Achieve Them." All of the concepts throughout the book are intertwined. Because nothing in a relationship happens in isolation, it is important to nurture all aspects of your relationship.

Feathering Your Nest is a guide and a workbook for you to share with your lover. It is meant to bring the two of you to a better understanding of yourselves and the bond that holds you together. The book is dedicated to all lesbians who are joined in life's journey and who sincerely want to stay together in a happy and healthy long-term relationship. The book has not served its function, however, if you move through it without having fun!

AND WHAT IS A PLA ANYWAY?

At times you'll see reference made to either PLA workshops, surveys, interviews, or participants. *PLA* refers to the Positive Living Alliance, an organization which the authors of *Feathering Your Nest* have founded. PLA provides workshops to various groups of people, especially lesbian communities in the Southeast region of the United States, who are interested in bringing positive change into their lives. The names of the PLA participants who are mentioned in the various anecdotes throughout the book have been changed to assure their privacy.

AND SO...

In the face of all possible obstacles, lesbian couples keep making a go of it. We keep coming together and setting up house. The fact of the matter is that the obstacles discussed in the introduction, and those unique ones that exist in your relationship, **can** be hurdled. Unfortunately, wanting success in a relationship is not enough; you have to be willing to sincerely work on it. It's important to devote as much attention to your relationship — one of the most crucial aspects of your existence — as you do to your job, your clothing, your car, or whatever other top priorities you have in life. Without proper attention, and without a firm belief in the possibility of a healthy long-term relationship, the bond has little chance of holding. If you are willing to do what it takes, however, you can feather a warm, sweet nest filled not only with love and devotion, but also with fun and excitement.

WHAT'S AHEAD?

As you move through *Feathering Your Nest*, keep in mind the following points:

- Your relationship has a much better chance of surviving
    if you feel good about being the lesbian that you are.
- Healthy relationships take time to develop.
- Relationships should not be left to fend for themselves;
    they need attentive nurturing on a continual basis.
- You **can** have a happy, exciting long-term relationship
    if you believe that you can.

If Your Home Life Radiates Happiness, All Other Areas of Your Life Will Take on the Glow!

FEATHERING YOUR NEST

An Interactive Workbook
and Guide to a
Loving Lesbian Relationship

Gwen Leonhard, M.Ed.
& Jennie Mast, MSW, BCSW

RISING
TIDE
PRESS

1997

GET THE DIALOGUE GOING

One of the most exciting aspects of a relationship is getting to know your partner. If you're both vibrant, growing individuals, there will always be something new to learn. Since one of the most important keys to a healthy partnership is clear communication, you need to get the dialogue going. The basic premise of *Feathering Your Nest* is, in fact, the importance of getting to know each other better in all areas of your relationship.

Do You Really Know Her That Well?

Before you begin on the first exercise of the book, which will involve questions about various specific aspects of daily living, consider some of the broad questions in the five categories presented below:

SOCIAL:

Your social life helps keep you connected to the rest of the world. This is where your friends are. This is where you have fun doing whatever it is that you enjoy doing. Have you considered some of the following questions concerning the type of social life you will be sharing with your partner?

1. Do the two of you share the same friends?
2. Do you like your partner's friends?

      3. Would you rather spend time alone with
           your lover or with other people?
      4. Does your partner enjoy the same
           types of activities that you enjoy?

It's important that the two of you can agree on the type of social life you want to share. Certainly you don't have to enjoy 100% of the same social activities, but conflicts can develop, for example, when one of you is a homebody and the other is a party animal.

SEXUAL:

Sexual intimacy is a great way to express your feelings for your partner, and is also a delightful way to relieve stress and share physical pleasure. Consider some of the following questions related to sexual intimacy in your life:

      1. Are you able to discuss your sexual needs
           and desires with your partner?
      2. Do you both have the same expectations in
           the bedroom?
      3. Are you both open to sexual experimentation?
      4. Do you have clear guidelines about sexual
           fidelity or even flirting with other people?

Especially in the area of sex, it is important to be clear and direct about your expectations. One of you may get involved with someone outside of the relationship and come back later with an "I didn't know." Unfortunately, sex seems to be the most difficult subject for couples to discuss comfortably and honestly.

FINANCIAL:

Most of us don't particularly like thinking about finances, but it's a crucial part of life. According to studies on why couples argue and even separate, financial discord has usually topped the list. Having the same financial goals and views on money would be ideal, but the ideal is not always an option. Although there are many areas of financial consideration, think about the following questions:

1. Will you maintain separate finances or will
    you merge your finances?

2. Does one of you try to save money while the
    other spends it freely?

3. Do you have a financial plan which will provide for the following:
    a. purchasing a new car if yours breaks down
    b. repair or replacement of the television or stereo or essential
       appliances
    c. loss of job
    d. medical, dental and vision checkups
    e. accident or long-term illness
    f. retirement

4. Do you want to provide for your partner in a will or with life insurance?

Many lesbians, especially young ones, don't want to concern themselves with
financial issues since "Money isn't important. Love is what's important." Although
the sentiment is sweet, most of us are well aware that love does not pay for a breast
exam or the rent or mortgage.

BIOLOGICAL FAMILIES:

Many of our families play some role in our lives. How much of a role they play is
often up to us. When they are supportive of who we are, they can be wonderful
assets to our lives. When they are closed-minded and critical of who we are, they can
be hurtful. Consider the following questions:

1. Do your families accept your relationship?
2. Do you have to de-dyke your home when they come to visit?
3. Are you invited into the home of your partner's family?

In addition to the families in which they were raised, many lesbians come to relationships with a child or children of their own; others come to relationships wanting a child or children of their own. These circumstances, which certainly involve biological family, present a whole new set of concerns that had best be discussed before making a serious commitment. For example, if your lover has a child from a previous relationship, with whom does the child live? Will you want to, or be expected to, provide for this child financially and/or emotionally? If your lover wants to have a child, do you agree to help raise it? Would you go through a sperm bank or will you involve a man whom you know and trust, or only a man whom you've met but don't know well? Do you want the father to be a part of the child's life? Discussing these various options concerning children is crucial to the survival of your relationship. Have a clear understanding of what you both are willing to forfeit or compromise on, and what you expect in these areas.

SPIRITUAL:

If you and your partner share all of the same religious beliefs, the same code of ethics and the same moral philosophies, you're unique. Most of us have opposing opinions on at least a few of the issues involving our "souls." Consider the following questions:

1. Do either you or your partner desire the other to attend religious services?
2. Does the doctrine of your faith condemn your lesbian lifestyle? If so, how does this make you feel about yourself and your relationship?
3. Does the doctrine of your faith condemn abortion, capital punishment or euthanasia?

Conflicts might develop between a couple if their spiritual-belief system differs from their actual living practices, or from the belief system of one of the partners. Some couples allow each other the right to retain their own personal philosophy without trying to influence it. In other relationships, there is a constant struggle to change one partner or the other. The further apart the religious and moral philosophies, the more frail the link that binds you.

The best way to avoid heartache later on in your relationship is to get the dialogue going NOW!

The wonderful thing about having different thoughts and opinions from our partners is that it allows us to explore ideas with fresh insight and a new perspective. Just because you and your partner don't agree on all of the issues outlined doesn't mean that you can't make your relationship work. It's important to decide together which differences your relationship can handle and which it can't. Weigh the blessings and the blight! And as will be suggested throughout the book, before you decide to terminate a relationship that you would very much like to keep, make sure you've discussed the issues honestly and completely with your partner. If that fails, please consider couple counseling with a lesbian-friendly professional.

GROUND RULES FOR A LOVING DIALOGUE

You and your partner are two distinct individuals with different perspectives and backgrounds. And since you will have to make innumerable personal decisions as you travel through life together, it's important to establish clear lines of communication. Relationships have a much better chance of surviving if both partners adhere to just three ground rules. Try using these rules for a loving dialogue as you approach different issues that arise in your home:

- **Express your feelings and thoughts openly and clearly.**

- **Listen carefully and respectfully.**

- **Be willing to compromise when your personal values are not threatened.**

Unless you express your feelings and thoughts openly and clearly with your partner, there is not much of a chance for her to understand what your needs and desires are. You have a right to whatever it is you feel and you have a right to express it. Allow yourself to share your feelings with your partner. If you have had negative experiences in the past when you have tried to express your feelings and thoughts to her, discuss *that*. If she doesn't make an effort to provide you with a safe, risk-free forum for self-expression, seek counseling.

According to PLA surveys of lesbians throughout the United States, when asked to identify the #1 frustration in their relationships, they overwhelmingly responded that they often felt they were not heard by their partners. Attentive listening is when you try to put yourself in her place and when you push aside your own feelings and thoughts long enough to hear what is actually being said. Careful and respectful listening is an act of love. When it comes to listening, you need to ask yourself two questions:

1. Do I respect my partner's thoughts and feelings?
2. Do I believe there is something to learn from what my partner has to say?

Hopefully your answer to both questions is a resounding YES! After all, it is only when you and your partner respect each other and believe there is something to learn from each other that effective communication can take place.

When you're in a healthy relationship, there are often times when you'll have to make decisions for the partnership rather than for just yourself. Be willing to compromise in the name of love. If she really wants to spend more time at home alone with you and if you really want to spend more time going out to dance and dine, make your best attempt at finding a middle ground, a place where you can both be satisfied.

Since communication is so important, we'll talk more about it later in the book, especially in the chapters "Fight Honorably" and "Problem-Solve as a Couple." In the interim, express your feelings, listen attentively and negotiate differences.

The Delight of Love
Is In The Coming Together

BRIEF DIRECTIONS FOR EXERCISES:

A variety of exercises are included to help you learn about yourselves and each other. In the case where each of you is asked to write down answers separately, please note that every exercise has been duplicated; therefore, you will see an exercise with the letter A following it and, either further down the page or on the next page, you will see the same exercise with the letter B following it. We recommend that you **not** look at your partner's answers before you have written down your own responses.

In each exercise, a space will be provided for your names. Do not fight over who will be A and who will be B; the letters are arbitrary and meaningless except for the fact that they let you know where the other person starts giving her answers. So decide now which letter you want to represent you for the purpose of responding to the exercises. Write down your names now!

PARTNER A:_____

PARTNER B:_____

The exercises that you and your partner do together will not have the letter A or B designated.

The following two exercises are for you and your lover to see how well you know each other. For some of you, you will find out plenty of new things about your lover; for others, you will find out that you know your lover pretty well. There are no right or wrong answers! Have fun!

Exercise #1-A

Name _____

Do this exercise separately from your partner. The exercise consists of questions that reveal your knowledge of yourself and your lover in many areas of daily living. On the first line, write in your own response to the question; on the second line, write how you think your lover might respond to the same question. **Exercise #1-B** following this exercise is for your partner to complete. When both of you are finished with all of **Exercise #1**, come together, compare answers, and get the dialogue going.

You might want to use some of the following answers to fill in your blanks: YES, NO, NOT SURE, ALWAYS, OFTEN, SOMETIMES, HARDLY EVER, NEVER.

	YOU	YOUR PARTNER
1. Do you exercise regularly?	_____	_____
2. Do you like to fall asleep with the TV or radio on?	_____	_____
3. Does it bother you to be affectionate in front of others?	_____	_____
4. Would you like to be told "I love you" more often?	_____	_____
5. Are you cheerful when you get up in the morning?	_____	_____
6. If you have a job, are you happy with it?	_____	_____

	YOU	YOUR PARTNER
7. Would you like to continue or go back to school?	_____	_____
8. Do you like to read?	_____	_____
9. Do you like to travel?	_____	_____
10. Do you sing around the house or in the shower?	_____	_____
11. Do you swear or curse?	_____	_____
12. Do you enjoy watching comedies?	_____	_____
13. Do you enjoy watching romantic movies?	_____	_____
14. Do sad movies make you cry?	_____	_____
15. Are you generous?	_____	_____
16. Do you like to share the shower with your lover?	_____	_____
17. Do you like to cook?	_____	_____
18. Do you keep a to-do list to remind you of things to be done?	_____	_____
19. Do you enjoy watching sports on TV?	_____	_____

	YOU	YOUR PARTNER
20. Do you enjoy attending sporting events?		
21. Would you feel comfortable having a loaded gun in your home?		
22. Is it important to spend the holidays with your biological family?		
23. Is it important to be with your partner on holidays?		
24. Will your partner be included in family gatherings?		
25. Will your partner be included in socials related to your job?		
26. Will you invite your partner to attend your high school or college reunion with you?		
27. Are you jealous of any of your partner's past relationships?		
28. Are you critical of your lover?		
29. Do you compliment your partner?		

	YOU	YOUR PARTNER
30. Do you ever want to get pregnant or bring a child into the relationship?	_____	_____
31. Do you want a joint savings account with your partner?	_____	_____
32. Do you want a joint checking account with your partner?	_____	_____
33. Does it bother you to be around cigarette smoke?	_____	_____
34. Do you allow people to smoke in your home?	_____	_____
35. Does it bother you to be around people using marijuana or other drugs?	_____	_____
36. Do you enjoy spending time with your friends apart from your partner?	_____	_____
37. Do you have positive feelings about your partner's family?	_____	_____
38. Do you criticize members of your partner's family?	_____	_____
39. Do you criticize your partner's friends?	_____	_____

	YOU	YOUR PARTNER
40. Do you use the words "Please" and "Thank you" with your lover?	_____	_____
41. If your partner had to move to another city, would you be willing to move also?	_____	_____
42. Are you "out" to the significant people in your life?	_____	_____
43. If your partner wanted you to convert to her religion, would you?	_____	_____
44. Who initiates sexual intimacy?	_____	_____
45. Have you been unfaithful in a previous relationship?	_____	_____
46. Do you share a fulfilling sex life?	_____	_____
47. Do you say things that hurt your partner's feelings?	_____	_____
48. Does your partner say things that hurt your feelings?	_____	_____
49. Do you ever pleasantly surprise your lover with gifts or actions?	_____	_____
50. Are you willing to work on the relationship when things get boring or difficult?	_____	_____

PARTNER A:
DO NOT GO BEYOND THIS POINT!

The next few pages are a duplication of Exercise #1 for your partner to complete.

Exercise #1-B

Name_____

Do this exercise separately from your partner. The exercise consists of questions that reveal your knowledge of yourself and your lover in many areas of daily living. On the first line, write in your own response to the question; on the second line, write how you think your lover might respond to the same question. When both of you are finished with all of **Exercise #1**, come together, compare answers, and get the dialogue going.

You might want to use some of the following answers to fill in your blanks: YES, NO, NOT SURE, ALWAYS, OFTEN, SOMETIMES, HARDLY EVER, NEVER.

	YOU	YOUR PARTNER
1. Do you exercise regularly?	_____	_____
2. Do you like to fall asleep with the TV or radio on?	_____	_____
3. Does it bother you to be affectionate in front of others?	_____	_____
4. Would you like to be told "I love you" more often?	_____	_____

	YOU	YOUR PARTNER
5. Are you cheerful when you get up in the morning?	_____	_____
6. If you have a job, are you happy with it?	_____	_____
7. Would you like to continue or go back to school?	_____	_____
8. Do you like to read?	_____	_____
9. Do you like to travel?	_____	_____
10. Do you sing around the house or in the shower?	_____	_____
11. Do you swear or curse?	_____	_____
12. Do you enjoy watching comedies?	_____	_____
13. Do you enjoy watching romantic movies?	_____	_____
14. Do sad movies make you cry?	_____	_____
15. Are you generous?	_____	_____
16. Do you like to share the shower with your lover?	_____	_____
17. Do you like to cook?	_____	_____

	YOU	YOUR PARTNER
18. Do you keep a to-do list to remind you of things to be done?	_____	_____
19. Do you enjoy watching sports on TV?	_____	_____
20. Do you enjoy attending sporting events?	_____	_____
21. Would you feel comfortable having a loaded gun in your home?	_____	_____
22. Is it important to spend the holidays with your biological family?	_____	_____
23. Is it important to be with your lover on holidays?	_____	_____
24. Will your partner be included in family gatherings?	_____	_____
25. Will your partner be included in socials related to your job?	_____	_____
26. Will you invite your partner to attend your high school or college reunion with you?	_____	_____

	YOU	YOUR PARTNER
27. Are you jealous of any of your partner's past relationships?	_____	_____
28. Are you critical of your partner?	_____	_____
29. Do you compliment your partner?	_____	_____
30. Do you ever want to get pregnant or bring a child into your relationship?	_____	_____
31. Do you want a joint savings account with your partner?	_____	_____
32. Do you want a joint checking account with your partner?	_____	_____
33. Does it bother you to be around cigarette smoke?	_____	_____
34. Do you allow people to smoke in your home?	_____	_____
35. Does it bother you to be around people using marijuana or other drugs?	_____	_____
36. Do you enjoy spending time with your friends apart from your partner?	_____	_____

	YOU	YOUR LOVER
37. Do you have positive feelings about your partner's family?		
38. Do you criticize members of your partner's family?		
39. Do you criticize your partner's friends?		
40. Do you use the words "Please" and "Thank you" with your partner?		
41. If your partner had to move to another city, would you be willing to move also?		
42. Are you "out" to the significant people in your life?		
43. If your lover wanted you to convert to her religion, would you?		
44. Who usually initiates sex?		
45. Have you been unfaithful in a previous relationship?		
46. Do you and your partner share a fulfilling sex life?		
47. Do you say things that might hurt your partner's feelings?		

	YOU	YOUR PARTNER
48. Does your partner say things that hurt your feelings?	_____	_____
49. Do you ever pleasantly surprise your partner with gifts or actions?	_____	_____
50. Are you willing to work on the relationship when things get boring or difficult?	_____	_____

After you have both completed the questions in Exercise #1, come together and discuss your findings. Perhaps you might consider gently tearing or cutting Exercise #1-B from the book so that you won't have to keep flipping pages. This might make looking at and talking about the answers a little less awkward physically.

Again, there are no right or wrong answers to the previous exercise. Perhaps in your discussions you've learned something new about your partner; perhaps she has learned something new about you. Use the new knowledge to enhance your relationship. If you learned that your partner would like to go back to school, you might discuss how the two of you could make that wish possible. If you learned that your partner is jealous of one of your previous relationships, perhaps you could reassure her of your devotion to her.

Once you've finished discussing Exercise #1 and you're feeling pretty secure in your knowledge of your lover, try the next exercise. It's a little tougher. Good luck.

INTERESTS AND HOBBIES

Exercise #2-A

Name_____

Separately answer the following about your lover, **without conferring**.

NAME YOUR LOVER'S:

favorite 2 television shows   _____

_____

favorite 2 movies   _____

_____

favorite restaurant   _____

favorite 2 songs   _____

_____

favorite book   _____

2 best friends   _____

_____

2 primary interests
    or hobbies   _____

_____

Exercise #2-B

Name _____

Separately answer the following about your lover, **without conferring.**

NAME YOUR LOVER'S:

favorite 2 television shows   _____

                                     _____

favorite 2 movies   _____

                                     _____

favorite restaurant   _____

favorite 2 songs   _____

                                     _____

favorite book   _____

2 best friends   _____

                                     _____

2 primary interests or hobbies   _____

                                     _____

Come together and see how well you know one another. What you didn't know before, hopefully you are finding out now. That's what's important!

Exercise #3

This is an exercise for you to do together as a couple. Some couples will get the answers correct immediately; others will perhaps squabble over minor differences in memory. If you do squabble here, keep it playful. ✍

What is the date of your anniversary? _____

Where did you first meet? _____

Where did you go on your first date? _____

Did you share a favorite song? What was it? _____

Partner A: Describe the circumstances of your first kiss. ✍

_____

_____

_____

Partner B: Describe the circumstances of your first kiss. ✍

_____

_____

_____

Your history together is important. Hopefully together you can recreate the feelings about the "firsts" in your relationship. Once you begin remembering the details, the feelings are often easily recollected. The problem that many people have is deciding on the actual date of their anniversary. Do you start with the day you first met or with the first "official" date or with the first kiss? Pick one or, better yet, celebrate all of those "firsts." What is important is that you celebrate the fact that you are together now! The birth of your relationship was and is a special time. It represents your hopes, your desires, and your passion for one another.

TOGETHER, FORGE YOUR OWN HISTORY!

$\blacktriangleright$ ~ 2 ~ $\blacktriangleleft$

MAKE A REAL COMMITMENT

When you make a real commitment to your lover, you are promising to nurture your partnership together with love, respect and devotion, through the good times and the bad. Although a relationship often involves compromise and selflessness, your individuality should be maintained and cultivated.

Before making a commitment, it would be an excellent idea to ask yourself the following two questions:

1. **Am I happy and fulfilled with my own life?**

2. **Is my potential partner happy and fulfilled with her own life?**

If you answered "No" to either of the two questions, you may want to postpone the commitment. Relationships are unfairly burdened when individuals enter them with the hopes of becoming happy and fulfilled. If you are committing yourself to a relationship because you're afraid of being alone, or because your former lover has found someone new, or because you're thinking, "Now I'll be happy," or for any other needy reason, you're not ready for a relationship. Be aware that not all women are ready for a serious commitment. In fact, *you* may not be ready.

Consider a woman with the following characteristics:

- Abuses drugs or alcohol;
- Is verbally or physically abusive;
- Is strangely secretive or in any way deceptive;
- Isn't sure if she's "really a lesbian";
- Finds joy in unhappiness.

Women with these and similar characteristics are often charming and lovable. Without first resolving their own problems, however, such women and those with similar characteristics are in no position to commit to another person. Although many women believe that they are capable of changing the "unhealthy" woman and of making her well, the truth is this rarely happens. The chances of successful reformation are slim without serious determination on the part of the woman herself, and/or without professional intervention.

Conversely, there are many women in the world who are ready to commit to a healthy lesbian relationship. Don't allow insignificant differences to prevent you from finding the right woman for you. It doesn't matter what color or nationality a woman is, how "cute" she looks, how young or old she is (as long as she's legal), how much money she has, etc. What does matter is that you make a commitment to someone who is happy and fulfilled with her own life and who is capable of enriching your life by being in it. Ask yourself: Does she help you to like yourself and the world more?

It is best to make your commitment from the head and not the heart. Does that surprise you? It sounds so unromantic! To make a commitment with another person simply because you're "in love" is like buying a house wholly because it has plenty of windows. Although the windows allow a cool breeze and radiant sunshine to enter the house and although the spaciousness makes you feel refreshed and serenely happy, there are other considerations. Should it matter that the slab is irreparably cracked, that the roof leaks when it rains, that the house is too small for your needs, and that it is overpriced? Unless you discover and explore the possible flaws in the relationship (not necessarily flaws in either you or the other person as individuals, but flaws in the combination of the two of you together), it won't be long before your bond becomes painful and frustrating. That's why it is best not to let your emotions lead you blindly into what could easily become a hellish situation. Base your decision on a rational consideration of what each of you wants in life, what each of you needs, and what each of you expects from the other. Falling in love with a person is absolutely *not* the sole reason to make a commitment. Get to know the person. Although no one is perfect, will you be able to live with those little "faults" that pop up after you've spent considerable time around the person with whom you're choosing to spend your life? Remember: Those early feelings of being head-over-heels in love are mostly temporary; they will probably fade somewhat. The feelings that develop in place of those early feelings are more loving and peaceful. Don't feel distressed. The "you-make-me-weak-in-the-knees" excitement will still exist when you properly nurture your relationship; it just won't be as exhaustingly constant as in the early days.

It's a healthy decision to ditch all of those mental homophobic tapes that play old, destructive songs like:
> "Lesbian relationships don't last,"
> "Oh, my relationships *never* seem to work out,"
> "*If* we break up, let's always be friends,"
> "*If* we're still together in three years, I'd like to..."
> "I want a relationship, but I don't want to have to work at it," and
> "I'll leave her before she leaves me."

Playing these old mental swan songs seems to reinforce the belief that lesbian relationships do not work out. Married heterosexual couples, even though they certainly don't always stay together, don't usually say things like, "*If* we're still together in three years, I'd like to...," or "*If* we break up, let's always be friends." Although heterosexual couples do break up, they don't gear themselves up for it in the same way that gay and lesbian couples do. The point is this: If you're suffering from internal homophobia, the likelihood of succeeding at a healthy lesbian relationship is slim. Because being a lesbian is who you are, and because feeling good about yourself is a prerequisite to making a serious commitment with another person, it is critical first to feel good about being a lesbian and about your chances at succeeding in your relationship.

DEFINING THE TERMS OF THE COMMITMENT

Before making a commitment, it's important for you and your lover to clearly define the boundaries of the relationship. Don't assume that both of you have the same expectations. What was acceptable in a past relationship, for example, may not be acceptable in the present one. Talking to one another openly at the outset of a relationship can help you prevent problems from occurring later.

Marleen, a PLA workshop participant, went out with some of her co-workers after work one day for a couple of beers. When she returned home two hours later than usual, her partner Nell was upset that Marleen hadn't called to let her know about the plans and that she hadn't been included in those plans in the first place. In Marleen's previous relationship, her partner didn't have a problem with Marleen's occasional outings after work or with the fact that she wasn't included in the plans. Marleen assumed that Nell wouldn't have a problem with these things either. Although they were able to work out an amicable compromise, they could have avoided the potentially hurtful situation if they had discussed the expectations and boundaries of their relationship beforehand.

Exercise #4-A

Name_____

Separately from your partner, check the column that most closely represents your answer to the following questions:

	YES	NO	NOT SURE
1. Do you expect your partner to be sexually faithful?	___	___	___
2. Would you end the relationship if your partner was not sexually faithful?	___	___	___
3. Are there major differences (e.g., economic, intellectual, cultural) that might possibly present a recurring problem?	___	___	___

Exercise #4A Continued

	YES	NO	NOT SURE

4. Will you conceal or lie about your sexual preference to significant people in your life? ___ ___ ___

5. Will you expect your partner to conceal or lie about her sexual preference to these people? ___ ___ ___

6. Do your friends and family respect your relationship? ___ ___ ___

7. Would it bother you if your partner went with friends to have a drink or play pool at a lesbian bar? ___ ___ ___

8. Would it bother you if your partner went with friends to have a drink or play pool at a straight bar? ___ ___ ___

9. Would you expect your partner to call if she were going to be late coming home? ___ ___ ___

10. Would you expect your partner to let you know where she will be when she is not with you? ___ ___ ___

11. Will former lovers be welcomed into your circle of friends? ___ ___ ___

12. Are you willing to make changes in your own behavior to improve your relationship? ___ ___ ___

Exercise # 4-B
Name_____

Separately from your partner, check the column that most closely represents your answer to the following questions:

	YES	NO	NOT SURE
1. Do you expect your partner to be sexually faithful?	___	___	___
2. Would you end the relationship if your partner was not sexually faithful?	___	___	___
3. Are there major differences (e.g., economic, intellectual, cultural) that might possibly present a recurring problem?	___	___	___
4. Will you conceal or lie about your sexual preference to significant people in your life?	___	___	___
5. Will you expect your partner to conceal or lie about her sexual preference to these people?	___	___	___
6. Do your friends and family respect your relationship?	___	___	___
7. Would it bother you if your partner went with friends to have a drink or play pool at a lesbian bar?	___	___	___
8. Would it bother you if your partner went with friends to have a drink or play pool at a straight bar?	___	___	___
9. Would you expect your partner to call if she were going to be late coming home?	___	___	___
10. Would you expect your partner to let you know where she will be when she's not with you?	___	___	___
11. Will former lovers be welcomed into your circle?	___	___	___
12. Are you willing to make changes in your own behavior to improve your relationship?	___	___	___

After completing the previous exercises, come together and discuss your answers. Know that these are only a few issues that you may have to face in your relationship. Do you have the same expectations? If you don't agree on all of the issues, can you reach a compromise? Is it easy to discuss your feelings and thoughts on potentially controversial issues? You not only have the right to know your partner's expectations of the relationship before making a commitment, you have the responsibility to know. If you and your partner are clear on what is expected, your relationship has a better chance of surviving.

THE ISSUE OF TRUST

Trust is the key ingredient to a successful relationship. If you examine the cause of problems in any relationship, you may just find that trust is the underlying issue in most of them.

It takes work to develop the necessary trust. If you are to have a healthy relationship, it is important to believe that your partner will not purposely hurt you and that she will protect your honor as she would her own, that she will be honest, loyal and reliable. However, do not expect her to do more for you than she would do for herself. You should not believe, for example, that she will honor her commitments to you if she does not honor commitments to herself. This is why it's important to take the early phases of your relationship slowly so that you can get to know your partner's behavioral patterns and what you can reasonably expect from her.

If you are to trust, you will have to forgive past offenses such as the infidelities of your previous lovers (if you have any) or even the infidelities of your present lover. Whether trust has been chiseled away a little at a time or blasted to pieces in one big betrayal, distrust produces an inescapable fear within a relationship. This fear, if allowed to fester, eventually replaces love and destroys the joy and stability of the bond. This does not mean that you should trust blindly. During the early phases of your relationship, you became aware of areas where you could, for the most part, trust your partner and other areas where you couldn't. While growing together as a couple, each of you has tested the waters on issues of trust, hopefully, with positive results. When trust is missing from a relationship and the couple can't seem to move closer to attaining it, professional counseling may be the answer. Trust issues vary so extensively that it would be impossible to deal with all aspects here.

Exercise #5

Together with your partner, discuss how each of you would respond to the following questions:

DO YOU TRUST THAT YOUR PARTNER WILL...

	YES	NO	NOT SURE
1. tell you the truth about her feelings and actions?	___	___	___
2. give you space to develop as an individual?	___	___	___
3. keep promises she makes to you?	___	___	___
4. be there when you need her?	___	___	___
5. work to improve the relationship?	___	___	___

Although there are many aspects to the issue of trust, the ones touched on in the previous exercise are especially important in maintaining a healthy and secure relationship. If either of you marked the "NO" column, your relationship could be in serious trouble. If you and your partner cannot find a way to establish trust in all five areas presented in Exercise #5, seek professional counseling. All five areas are crucial to the very foundation of your relationship.

Comments: ✎

IT'S REASONABLE FOR YOU TO WANT TO KNOW THAT YOUR PARTNER...

1. reveals to you *relevant* truths about her feelings and actions;
2. wants you to develop into the best person you can be;
3. keeps her promises to you;
4. is available to you, when possible, in times of need (e.g., family tragedies, illness, emergencies, personal conflicts); and
5. wants your relationship to succeed and is willing to make changes to assure the success of your relationship.

You're not expecting too much when you expect these five elements; they are your right within the relationship. Of course there are extenuating circumstances that may prevent you or your partner from living up to them (i.e. illness, temporary physical separation). For example, if your lover promises to take you out to dinner and then finds out her ill mother needs her help, it is not unreasonable for her to change the plans with you in order to help her mother. Similarly, if you have a fleeting thought of another woman waft through your head during the day, it would be unfair to come home and report the thought to your lover.

Exercise #6-A

Name_____

Separately from your partner, answer the following questions:

Have you ever...

	YES	CROSSED MY MIND	NO
1. secretly followed your partner to see where she was going?	____	____	____
2. passed by the place your lover said she would be to see if she was really there?	____	____	____

	YES	CROSSED MY MIND	NO
3. passed by a place where you thought your partner might be?	——	——	——
4. called the place she said she'd be to make sure that it was true?	——	——	——
5. eavesdropped on your partner's phone conversation?	——	——	——
6. not given your partner a phone message on purpose?	——	——	——
7. opened your partner's mail?	——	——	——
8. gone through your partner's pockets, glove compartment, etc., looking for clues?	——	——	——
9. gone through receipts, canceled checks or credit card statements looking for suspicious charges?	——	——	——
10. considered hiring a detective to check up on your partner?	——	——	——

Exercise #6-B
Name_____

Separately from your partner, answer the following questions:

Have you ever...

	YES	CROSSED MY MIND	NO
1. secretly followed your partner to see where she was going?	___	___	___
2. passed by the place your lover said she would be to see if she was really there?	___	___	___
3. passed by a place where you thought your partner might be?	___	___	___
4. called the place she said she'd be to make sure that it was true?	___	___	___
5. eavesdropped on your partner's phone conversations	___	___	___
6. not given your partner a phone message on purpose?	___	___	___
7. opened your partner's mail?	___	___	___
8. gone through your partner's pockets, drawers, etc., looking for clues?	___	___	___
9. gone through receipts, canceled checks or credit card statements looking for suspicious charges?	___	___	___
10. considered hiring a detective to check up on your partner?	___	___	___

After you have both completed the exercise, discuss your responses with your partner and the possible reasons for those responses.

If you've done or thought of doing any of the actions in Exercise #6, it does not necessarily mean that your relationship is doomed to failure. Perhaps you're a bit cautious because of a past experience with an unfaithful partner. You might want to be aware, however, that these behaviors can have a destructive impact on your relationship, even if the suspicions are groundless. Consider why you feel the need to behave in such a non-trusting manner. Consider also how you might feel if the tables were turned and you were unfairly suspected of unfaithful behavior. On the other hand, if you think your suspicions could very well be warranted, you will want to openly discuss your feelings with your partner and perhaps even insist that the two of you seek professional counseling.

TRUST = RESPECT
For Yourself and Your Partner

There is no room for suspicious behavior in a truly trusting and respectful relationship. Frequently suspicions, even when based only on imagined indiscretions or infidelities, have the power to destroy a relationship faster than anything else. If you're giving your partner cause for suspicion, start behaving virtuously. If you are unreasonably suspicious of your partner, ask yourself why. Because your partnership should relieve stress in your life, not cause it, it is equally important for both of you to be able to rely on each other. Unless your relationship is based on trust, you may want to hold off on making a serious commitment or you may even want to reconsider the commitment you've made.

IN SUMMARY

You're probably ready to make a serious commitment, if...
- ❏ you are both happy and fulfilled as individuals;
- ❏ your commitment is made through rational thought rather than romantic emotion; and
- ❏ you believe that you are capable of maintaining a healthy, long-term relationship based on trust and love.

MAKING THE PLEDGE

Although making a sincere commitment doesn't guarantee that the relationship will last, the chances of failure are greatly reduced when both of you work at assisting each other in fulfilling your individual needs. Never lose sight of that. If you're going to make a commitment, invest fully. Invest spiritually. Invest emotionally. Invest physically. There will be ups and downs. Expect them. There will be times when you're not happy within the relationship. Expect that. This is not a signal for you to throw up your hands and walk away; rather, it is a signal for you to stick to your word and bring about positive changes that will make your relationship a happier reality.

Exercise #7

On the lines provided below, write down a conscious pledge to your partner letting her know that you are genuinely committed to her and to the relationship. You might write something like the following:

> I, (your name), sincerely commit myself to you, (her name).
> I join you in life to enhance your existence and my own.
> Because I genuinely love you, I will work to make our union
> happy and fulfilled.

Partner A   Name_____

Pledge of Commitment: ✍

_____

_____

_____

_____

_____

_____

_____

_____

_____

Partner B   **Name**_____

Pledge of Commitment: ✍

_____

_____

_____

_____

_____

_____

_____

Once you commit to each other, you're ready to move on to create a home and family. The words "home" and "family" are not ideas reserved just for heterosexuals! We can all share the dream.

 3

CREATE A HOME AND FAMILY

Once you have made a commitment with your lover, the two of you become a family. Yes, two people of the same sex can be a family in and of themselves. While growing up, you didn't have much of a choice about what kind of family you were part of, but you do now. How many times have you complained about the family in which you were raised? Now is your chance to create the family you want for yourself. What are you going to do differently? And if you grew up in a perfectly wonderful family, now is your opportunity to emulate that family. Create a home that is your safe haven, a place to which you can come home from a busy day on the job and feel happy, secure and loved. This is where feathering your nest begins. Create a home where you can share your dreams and hopes without fear. If you want a lasting and loving relationship with your partner, create an environment that satisfies the needs of both of you as individuals.

Feather Your Nest
With Dreams, Love And Laughter!

MEMBERS OF YOUR FAMILY

Having a sense of family provides warmth and security for many of us. While family can certainly include those people with whom we are biologically linked, it can also include those cherished friends who have become an important part of our lives.

Together with your lover, resolve to make a healthy family for yourselves. This may include all or some of the following:
  1. your actual biological families;
  2. your closest friends (whether straight or gay, whether male or female);
  3. your local lesbian and gay community:
     a. political and activist organizations;
     b. religious organizations;
     c. community centers;
     d. health/AIDS organizations;
     e. social and special interest groups;
        (e.g., artistic, athletic, volunteer, etc.);
  4. your dogs or cats or other animal companions.

At the center of all the decisions you make in life, the sacred bond between you and your partner will, hopefully, remain in the forefront of your mind. Make decisions that contribute to the stability and welfare of your relationship. In order to create a healthy and lasting bond, refrain from making decisions that contaminate your relationship with manipulative game-playing, cruel threats of desertion or outside intrusion, and all other disrespectful behaviors. Your core family now consists of you and your partner. Whoever enters into this core family with you should respect and enrich your lives. If one of you has a friend, for example, who always seems to drive a wedge between you and your partner, discuss the problem openly first with your partner and then with all parties involved. Make it clear that the potentially divisive behavior must cease. If all goes well, the bond of friendship will be strengthened. If the wedge driving continues, you will perhaps want to eliminate that "friend" from your lives. Remember that your core relationship is now between you and your partner. This relationship, first and foremost, is the one you must honor and protect. Just as you would want honor for yourself, you now have a responsibility to honor and protect the relationship of which you are a part.

Exercise #8

Together with your lover, list those individuals or groups of people who make up your family. *Make sure to name only those who enrich your life as a couple.* (If you can't think of ten people whom you would consider family, leave spaces blank and come back to it later if necessary. Perhaps you can think of more than ten. If so, write their names in the margins.)

YOUR VERY OWN FAMILY MEMBERS

1. _____   6. _____
2. _____   7. _____
3. _____   8. _____
4. _____   9. _____
5. _____   10. _____

Just as you create the family, you also create the dynamics that cause the relationships to provide what you and your partner need and want in order to be fulfilled each day of your lives together. This is not to say there won't be problems; there will always be one obstacle or another to hurdle. That is the nature of life! The difference will be that you'll work through the problems in a constructive and loving manner. Working through the inevitable problems as a team will hopefully bring you and your partner closer together. No matter what problems arise, however, your core family should feel safe. Feeling safe, by the way, is not the same as taking your partner for granted. In a safe family, there is no feeling of being used and there is no fear of abandonment or hostility; in a safe family, you can expect stability and love.

ESTABLISHING TRADITIONS

Once your new family has been created, establish your own family traditions. (Some traditions, of course, will come with you from your past, and some will create themselves.) The traditions can be events or customs that each of you look forward to sharing on a regular basis. Most families create traditions as a result of events and experiences, so many of your fondest memories will come into play here. Traditions are a sort of glue which helps hold the fabric of your relationship together.

Sarah and Jessica, a lesbian couple who participated in a Positive Living Alliance workshop, discussed a fun tradition they created. They planned a weekend trip to a national park where they could rent cabins. They invited both of their biological families to also rent cabins so that they could all spend the weekend together. Sarah and Jessica made the occasion much more than a quiet weekend in nature; they made it an extravaganza. The couple planned entertaining activities for everyone, children and adults alike. There was to be a costume party, a fishing trip, a kids' hike, a poker game, and so much more. They then sent out fun invitations to both of their families, outlining the planned activities. Several members of both their families rented cabins in anticipation of a weekend of fun. A great time was had by all. They are now going on their fifth year of the weekend jaunt to the park. Not only have their families become closer as a result of the weekend outings, but now they also eagerly join in the planning.

It was important to Sarah and Jessica to spend time with their biological families. Fortunately, they are both "out" to their families and are loved by each other's family. Unfortunately, not all lesbians enjoy the same open-arm policy (usually not through any fault of their own) with their biological families. If either of your families is intolerant of your lifestyle or of your lover, your traditions may include close friends instead. As stated previously, "family" is by no means limited to blood relations. If you celebrate Christmas or Thanksgiving, for example, you may want to fix a banquet or an outdoor picnic and invite those people who do accept and enrich your lives to share the holiday with you.

MEMORIES ARE MADE OF THIS

Beth and Marcia, another lesbian couple who participated in the workshop, share another family tradition with a mutual friend of theirs, Winnie. When Winnie comes into town about once a year, the three women go on a day-long photo shoot. They pack up cameras, film, tripods, sandwiches, and a bottle of wine. They then take off for the day. They go to a scenic location, such as the beach or the park, and snap away. The tradition, which has been going on for the past seven years, has resulted in some great photographs and great laughs. A few of the photos, which Beth and Marcia had enlarged and framed, now hang on the walls of the couple's home and often remind them of days of laughter and friendship.

Other traditions might include the following:

1. keeping photo/ memory books of places you travel together;
2. renting a movie every Tuesday night;
3. collecting matchbooks of restaurants in which the two of you have dined;
4. cooking together on Sunday evenings;
5. hosting a Halloween or New Year's Eve party annually;
6. celebrating your anniversary together;
7. having coffee on the front porch on Sunday mornings;
8. going on a planned date once a week;
9. reading the newspaper together in the evening after work;
10. watching a particular television show that you both enjoy;
11. having savings bonds issued in both of your names each month;
12. walking in the evenings after supper;
13. playing tennis on Saturday mornings;
14. going to the polls and voting together on election days;
15. going to the beach with your favorite other couple.

Notice that some of the traditions listed above occur yearly and others perhaps weekly or even nightly. Any act or event that you and your partner make part of your lives together can become a tradition. Create traditions that both of you look forward to and that make the bond between you more solid.

Exercise #9

Together with your partner, list three traditions that are part of **your** family.

1. _____

   _____

2. _____

   _____

3. _____

   _____

If you and your partner have just recently made a commitment to one another, don't feel downhearted if you don't have any recurring traditions yet. As you move through the years together, you can create traditions that belong to you, your partner, and the family that you choose to embrace. If your relationship is new, come back to this page in a year or two and fill in your traditions then. **Take Note:** The assumption is definitely that the two of you will still be together to come back to the exercise.

SYMBOLS OF YOUR AFFECTION

Similar to traditions are physical bonds or rituals that identify you and your partner as a couple. Straight people can have weddings; they often exchange rings; they can sign marriage certificates; they sometimes hold hands and kiss publicly; they usually pool their finances together; they often buy a house together; they usually have children. We know what they do; after all, they flaunt their lifestyle in front of us on a daily basis. Straight couples have many different ways to identify themselves as a legal marital unit. In recent years, lesbians, too, have begun to share some of those same physical expressions of their bonds. Lesbians often exchange rings; they have similar "wedding" ceremonies; they sometimes hold hands and kiss publicly; they sometimes pool their finances together; they sometimes buy houses together. Like some heterosexuals, there are some lesbians who have used tattooing and/or piercing to express the bond with their partner. To have physical bonds or rituals that say, "We are a couple" is a way to make visible and validate their union to one another and to society. Symbolic physical bonds or rituals can give the couple a concrete sense of singularity.

Exercise #10

List three symbolic bonds within your relationship that say, "**We are a couple**."

1. _____

2. _____

3. _____

While many married heterosexual women are opting to retain their maiden name instead of switching to their husband's name, some lesbians are choosing to legally change their last name to their partner's. Lisa and Joan, both participants in a Positive Living Alliance workshop, have been in a relationship for thirteen years. A couple of years ago, Lisa decided that she wanted to legally change her last name to Joan's. After discussing her desires with Joan and also with Joan's siblings, Lisa changed her name. All of the important people in their lives, including both of their biological families, were told about the name change. When Lisa's lover, Joan, told her mother what Lisa had done, her reaction was a surprised "Why did she do that? I don't think I'd change my name." Joan's response was, "But you did when you married Dad." She went on to explain to her mother that having the same last name simply makes Lisa feel more cohesion and more permanence within their relationship, a choice that Lisa made for herself. Lisa's name change was her way of saying, "We are a couple."

LEGAL PROTECTION

There are various legal strategies that lesbians can employ to make their union more "binding." There are some lesbians, for example, who are legally adopting their partners; and many others are filing for power of attorney over their partners; others are legally including partners in wills and contracts. Books dealing with the legalities of lesbian/gay relationships can be found in bookstores that cater to our population. Take a look at Curry and Clifford's *Legal Guide for Lesbians and Gay Men* for starters. If you and your partner decide to take one of the few legal avenues open to you, consult a knowledgeable lesbian-friendly attorney to assist you with the proceedings. You can also consult a local gay/lesbian organization or your local American Civil Liberties Union (ACLU) for help. Either one of these resources will be able to direct you to an attorney experienced in legal matters affecting you as a lesbian.

HOUSEHOLD CHORES

Another type of tradition is the maintaining of the household. This aspect of a relationship really gets down to the nitty gritty day-to-day grind. Just like in most traditional families, each of you hopefully makes contributions to the household. On the next two pages is an exercise for getting a clear look at who does what and how each person feels about the distribution of labor in your home.

Exercise #11

Together determine which duties are yours and which are your partner's. Are some of the duties shared by both of you? Put a check ✔ in the appropriate column. Be honest. (Yes, you can use percentages if checks don't tell the whole story!)

HOUSEHOLD DUTIES	Partner A	Partner B	Both A & B
General housecleaning			
Vacuuming/mopping			
Dusting/polishing furniture			
Scouring bathroom			
Washing and drying dishes			
Cooking meals			
Laundry chores			
Grocery shopping			
Yard work (mowing, weeding, etc.)			
Caring for pets			
Home repairs			
Paying the bills			
Paying the mortgage or rent			

Exercise #12-A

Name _____

Separately answer the following questions by circling the appropriate response:

1. Are you comfortable with the distribution of labor in your home?

>   No   Yes   Not Sure

2. Do you think your lover is comfortable with the distribution of labor?

>   No   Yes   Not Sure

3. Does the distribution of labor cause conflict in your home?

>   No   Yes   Not Sure

4. Is there any way to make the distribution of labor more amicable?

>   If NO, why?_____

>   _____

>   _____

>   _____

>   If YES, how?_____

>   _____

>   _____

>   _____

Exercise #12-B

Name_____

Separately answer the following questions and circle the appropriate response:

1. Are you comfortable with the distribution of labor in your home?

     No   Yes   Not Sure

2. Do you think your lover is comfortable with the distribution of labor?

     No   Yes   Not Sure

3. Does the distribution of labor cause conflict in your home?

     No   Yes   Not Sure

4. Is there any way to make the distribution of labor more amicable?

     If NO, why?_____

        _____

        _____

        _____

        _____

     If YES, how?_____

        _____

        _____

If either you or your lover has the feeling that the distribution of labor is unfair, many problems can surface in the relationship under many different guises. If your lover has the lion's share of the household labor, for instance, she may begin to resent you without even being conscious of the reason. Nobody likes feeling used!

Keep the dialogue open about the distribution of labor. Clear communication is vital. The distribution can be changed, rearranged, and often exchanged with little effort. It doesn't have to be a problem if you and your partner approach the arrangement with love and fairness.

SPOTLIGHT ON THE STRENGTHS

In the home that you create, it is important to focus on the strengths — your partner's and your own. When you do, many of the weak spots that do exist will vanish on their own. We humans don't flourish much when we are criticized, abused, berated and ridiculed. With the spotlight on strengths, you not only feel more worthwhile as an individual, you also feel closer to your partner and safer within your relationship. The inevitable problems that life will send your way will seem easier to handle because of that shared closeness. As a strong couple, you will be able to approach life's obstacles and snags with the self-assurance needed to move on together. Although there is cause to celebrate the similar strengths you and your partner share, there is even more of a cause to celebrate the dissimilar strengths. While unity can be encouraged by strengths, it can be equally reinforced by differences.

Exercise #13-A

Name_____

Complete this exercise separately from your partner. Consider the list below, but do not limit yourself to it. Then answer the questions that follow: ✍

diplomacy	order	practicality	humor
patience	loyalty	intelligence	dependability
flexibility	kindness	playfulness	spontaneity
thriftiness	romance	confidence	thoughtfulness
forgiveness	creativity	sociability	responsibility

1. What strengths do you bring to your relationship?

_____

_____

2. What strengths does your partner bring to your relationship?

_____

_____

3. Are your strengths the same? Circle the appropriate answer. **Yes No   Somewhat**

Comments: ✍

Exercise #13-B

Name_____

Complete this exercise separately from your partner. Consider the list below, but do not limit yourself to it. Then answer the questions that follow: ✍

diplomacy	order	practicality	humor
patience	loyalty	intelligence	dependability
flexibility	kindness	playfulness	spontaneity
thriftiness	romance	confidence	thoughtfulness
forgiveness	creativity	sociability	responsibility

1. What strengths do you bring to your relationship?

_____

_____

2. What strengths does your partner bring to your relationship?

_____

_____

3. Are your strengths the same? Circle the appropriate answer.   **Yes   No   Somewhat**

Comments: ✍

Exercise #14

Together, discuss the answers that you each wrote for Exercise #13. Also discuss the following considerations concerning your individual strengths:

1. How do the similar strengths contribute to your relationship?
2. How do the dissimilar strengths contribute to your relationship?
3. Were you drawn to your partner originally because of any of the strengths being discussed?
4. Have you ever thought of any of the strengths as problems within the relationship?
5. How can each of the strengths enrich your relationship?

Together, list the other differences that each of you has brought into your relationship. Consider age, race, nationality, religion, occupation, education, height, weight and any other notable differences.

Example:	Partner C	Partner D
	26 years old	41 years old
	Artist	Doctor
	Raised Jewish	Active Catholic
	Middle-class family	Upper-class family
	High school graduate	College graduate
	Loves to travel	Loves to be home
	Is 5' 2" tall	Is 5' 10"

And continue the list with as many differences as you can think of along these lines. If you can't come up with ten differences, come up with as many as you can. If you can come up with more than ten, continue in the margins.

Name_____   Name_____

        Partner A   Partner B

1.
2.
3.
4.
5.
6.
7.
8.
9.
10.

Many of the differences you have listed will probably not have much of a bearing on your relationship; however, others will. Which ones listed above are relevant to your bond? Which ones contribute — even in some odd way — to your bond? If you look back at the example related to Partners C and D, that couple might say that Partner C's talent in art has given her the knowledge and creativity to decorate their home in a fun and unique way, while Partner D's height allows her to reach the top shelves in their kitchen cabinets that are slightly out of Partner C's reach. Because of these seemingly innocuous differences, both partners are at an advantage.

Although many of us tend to focus on how the differences in our relationships cause problems, differences can actually contribute more to a relationship than the similarities. Your partner's differences will broaden your view of the world. When you think about it, it was probably the differences that attracted you to your lover in the first place. By appreciating and even nurturing those traits that make you distinct, you can add balance, power and zing to your union. Long live the difference!

Celebrate Your Differences!

GENERATE GOALS AND ACHIEVE THEM

Generating goals can encourage lesbian couples to expect their relationships to be happy, exciting and fulfilling, as well as long-lived. It is a key combatant in the battle against the negative programming of internalized homophobia. Clearly, goal-setting challenges the notion that lesbian relationships are somehow inferior to heterosexual ones and are doomed to be short-lived. That is why goals fill tomorrow with hope.

If You're Planning the Next Day of Your Relationship Together, You Must Expect It To Arrive

Before deciding which goals you and your partner want to reach, consider the values that you share together. You've both come to the relationship with different histories and different "baggage." Now the two of you will want to find a common road to travel together from this point onward. Your values will help direct you as you move along the road of life. If you and your partner are going in the same direction, you should be guided by many of the same values. This is not to suggest that you must give up your individuality in order to fuse totally with your partner. Although individual differences should be celebrated, a relationship has little chance of surviving if similarities don't exist to secure it.

In this chapter, you are asked to work on exercises that will determine the priorities or values that you and your partner share, and also how you would like to direct your life's journey. There are no right or wrong answers; therefore, don't feel compelled to put down an answer that might please your partner. Be honest.

Exercise #15-A

Name_____

Separately from your partner, select ten areas from the list below that are **most** important to you personally. Rank your selections by numbering them 1 through 10, with 1 being the most important and 10 being the least.

_____ Travel   _____ Owning your own home

_____ Career   _____ Living close to family/friends

_____ Social status   _____ Traditions within your home

_____ Sex   _____ Money/possessions

_____ Leisure time   _____ Personal independence

_____ Your lover/partner   _____ Children

_____ Spirituality   _____ Other _____

Exercise #15-B

Name_____

Separately from your partner, select ten areas from the list below that are **most** important to you personally. Rank your selections by numbering them 1 through 10, with 1 being the most important and 10 being the least.

_____ Travel   _____ Owning your own home

_____ Career   _____ Living close to family/friends

_____ Social status   _____ Traditions within your home

_____ Sex   _____ Money/possessions

_____ Leisure time   _____ Personal independence

_____ Your lover/partner   _____ Children

_____ Spirituality   _____ Other _____

Once both of you have completed the previous exercise, discuss the choices that each of you made. **Together**, compile one list of the top five values upon which you both hope to base your relationship. An example of a value could be: "Expanding our horizons by reading or traveling." The values should be listed below in the order of importance, with 1 being the most important and 5 being the least.

THE TOP 5 IMPORTANT VALUES GUIDING YOUR RELATIONSHIP

1. _____

2. _____

3. _____

4. _____

5. _____

As a couple, why did you decide these were the most important values? ✍

_____

_____

As a couple, did you experience any difficulty or uncomfortableness in selecting these five important values? ✍

_____

_____

In Exercise #16, you will be asked to focus on more specific areas of your life. Due to the nature of the exercise, it is a good time to remind you of the importance of compromise.

Exercise #16

Together, as a couple, prioritize each column of ten items according to which are most important to you **as a couple**, 1 indicating the **most** important and 10 indicating the **least** important.

People	Time	Money
___ Yourself	___ Sleep	___ Personal
___ Your lover/ partner	___ Work	___ Entertainment
___ Friends	___ Television	___ Clothing
___ Parents	___ Hobbies/ interests	___ Home
___ Nieces/nephews	___ Parents/family	___ Travel
___ Your own children	___ Household chores	___ Car
___ Business associates	___ Individual time alone	___ Medical
___ Neighbors	___ Time alone as a couple	___ Education
___ Clergy	___ House of worship	___ Savings Account
___ Other	___ Other	___ Other

Are your priorities the same? Were either of you willing to compromise any of your answers to better align them with your partner's? Are there any serious differences in values and priorities that can, and do, cause problems within your relationship? Can you work through those differences?

Consider the following situation. Rhonda has been living with Cathy for the past two years. Because Rhonda is very conservative with her money and Cathy is not, the money issue is a constant source of conflict in their relationship. It's important to Rhonda to save money in case of an emergency and for special plans (e.g., a trip to Hong Kong, the purchase of a home). Cathy, on the other hand, likes to spend her money on compact discs, clothes and magazines. According to Rhonda, Cathy spends her money as fast as she earns it. When Rhonda talks to Cathy about planning a vacation, though, Cathy says that she doesn't have the money. Rhonda feels resentful because vacationing wouldn't be the same without having Cathy along with her; and, at the same time, she feels that Cathy shouldn't have been spending her own money so "frivolously." Rhonda feels that Cathy keeps her from doing what she wants to do — go on a vacation with her partner! Neither of these two women is doing anything wrong; their priorities are just different. Perhaps the issue will eventually destroy their relationship or perhaps they can find a place to compromise.

Ideally, it's the compromise you're seeking. Without totally surrendering your own priorities and preferences, try to align them as closely as possible with your partner's. Compromise is a powerful tool in helping a relationship proceed beyond the frivolous.

Once you decide what life components are important to each of you and what both of you mutually want from the relationship, you can start creating goals. Think of the idea of "goal" as it relates to football or soccer. Ball players don't just wish to gain points; they plan out strategies and work toward that common objective. The exceptionally skilled teams methodically march down the field to tally up those points. They don't rely on those accidental fumbles or that last-minute point to push them over the top. The winning football and soccer teams know how to plan and how to carry out the plan in a thoughtful and skilled manner. You and your partner are a team. You, too, need to plan your strategies and work deliberately toward your goals. Expect success. If at first you fail to meet your goals, refocus your energies, alter your plan, and try again.

Some of you may be thinking, "I love sports, but a relationship shouldn't have to be so deliberate and thought out. It should be fun." Consider the following question: Which team do you think has the most fun, the goal-oriented one that wins, or the haphazard one that loses?

If you don't want life to just push you along aimlessly, you and your lover, as a couple, will want to make **deliberate** plans together for yourselves, each other, and this new life that you are determined to create. It's important that the plans be realistically attainable, that there are deadlines for the plans to be implemented, and that you can measure whether or not the goals have been achieved. It is imperative to write down your goals and then to keep them in view; after all, you don't want to lose sight of them if you intend to attain them. Post your mutual goals on the refrigerator, on the bathroom mirror, or on the inside of your closet door. It doesn't matter where you post them, so long as you don't lose sight of them.

SHORT-TERM GOALS

Start out with short-term goals. What do you and your lover expect to achieve within the next month? Rearranging the furniture, painting a table, quitting cigarette smoking, losing weight or gaining weight, spending more quality time together, saying something sweet or complimentary to your lover at least twice a day, making love more frequently, cleaning out your closet and donating clothes to a battered women's center or some other charitable organization, organizing a breast-cancer or AIDS support group or a social or a sports event within the community? Remember that there should be some observable way in which to tell if the goal has been achieved. Don't say, "We're going to do more physical exercise"; instead, be specific and say, "We're going to walk two miles at least four days a week."

Exercise #17

As a couple, list three goals in the spaces below that you and your lover want to achieve within the next month. Today's date: _____ ✍

    1. _____

    2. _____

    3. _____

LONG-TERM GOALS

After you have generated a one-month plan, reach out a bit further. What goals do you and your lover want to attain within the next year? Saving enough money to attend the Michigan Women's Music Festival or the Gay Pride festivities in New York or San Francisco, losing 20 pounds, "coming out" to all meaningful members of your existence, moving into a bigger apartment, doing volunteer work for a breast-cancer or AIDS support center on a regular basis, forming a rock band or a softball team, digging a pond and building a deck in your backyard, being promoted at work? Most of the goals listed here are goals that cannot be attained overnight. You might need to save money in advance, or lose one pound a week, or tell one important person in your life at a time that you're a lesbian. As long as you're moving toward the goal, it doesn't matter how long it takes you. Make sure that your movement forward is steady and that there is some way to tell if your goals are being reached.

Exercise #18

As a couple, list three goals in the spaces below that you and your lover want to achieve within the next year. Today's date: _____ ✍

1. _____

2. _____

3. _____

Reach further. What goals do you and your lover wish to achieve within the next three years? **Expect to be together.** Putting a down payment on a house, living in Paris for a few months, opening up your own business, getting a college degree, buying a recreational vehicle to tour the country? These may be a bit more difficult to achieve. You don't have to complete the following exercise in one sitting. Give yourselves some time to think about this one if you need to.

Exercise #19

Again as a couple, list two goals in the space below that you and your lover want to accomplish in the next five years. Today's date:＿＿＿＿＿＿ ✍

1. ＿＿＿＿＿＿＿＿＿＿＿＿＿＿＿＿＿＿＿＿＿＿＿＿＿＿＿＿＿＿＿＿＿

2. ＿＿＿＿＿＿＿＿＿＿＿＿＿＿＿＿＿＿＿＿＿＿＿＿＿＿＿＿＿＿＿＿＿

Goals create purpose and excitement. When you can plan your destiny and look forward to those events, those opportunities, those joys that are coming your way, then the journey of life becomes filled with sweet anticipation. Boredom doesn't have much of a chance against these odds.

HAVING GOALS IN LIFE GIVES EACH DAY PURPOSE!

If you fail to achieve any of your goals, examine the reason(s) for the failure. Perhaps you can attain your goal with a more specific plan or with additional steps. Commit yourself once again to reaching the goals that are important for you. Whatever you do, don't give up.

Feathering Your Nest focuses on strengthening the bonds between lesbian partners; but, it is also vital to work individually on your own personal goals, goals that you attain separately from your partner, goals that continually promote your own self-growth and keep you interesting and attractive as an individual. There's nothing more attractive, after all, than a person who has a passion for living, who has a meaningful purpose beyond the relationship.

Goal-setting need not take away from the spontaneity in a relationship. Leave spaces in your life for unplanned activities or non-activities. It's nice to be able to make the decision to go to bed early, to watch a television program, to read, or to just squander some time away. Sometimes it's delightful to just have nothing to do. Be flexible with your partner and yourself by being able to switch the proverbial gears of life without thinking, "But this is not what I had planned." Goal-setting need not keep you from enjoying the here and now. Although setting goals provides you with a future to eagerly anticipate, there is something to be said for relishing the moment. Make goal-setting an integral part of your relationship, but of course spice up your life with spontaneity and appreciation for the moment at hand.

If life is a journey, then plan where you want to go, what you want to experience, with whom you want to share it, and how you want to get to your various destinations. Who better to take control of the reins than you? Without planning and mapping out your way, you're going to miss out on many wonderful and rewarding experiences. Working on specific goals, after all, is the business of making dreams come true.

Exercise #20

Together with your lover, discuss the following two questions concerning your life together **as a couple**. Be as specific as possible. Today's date:_____ ✍

    1. What do you envision life to be like **ten** years from now?

_____

_____

_____

    2. What do you envision life to be like **twenty** years from now?

_____

_____

_____

Visualize the kind of life you'd like at both of these points in time.

    ● Are you comfortable with the fact that the shape of the future is molded by your own hands?

    ● Are you both willing to make your dreams into a reality?

There Must Be Laughter!
There Must Be Dreams!

5

FIGHT HONORABLY

Since you and your partner are two separate individuals with two entirely different brains which hold their own unique perceptions and thoughts, accept the fact that you will have conflicting points of view now and then. It's a given. You will not always agree with one another. What a refreshing thought! Furthermore, your lack of agreement will sometimes result in feelings of anger. Expect arguments to occur and expect to feel anger at times. Instead of allowing either the disagreement or the anger to destroy your relationship, handle them in such a way that your relationship will be more intimate and loving because of them. When you face conflicting feelings and thoughts, new and interesting doors will open for each of you. Allow yourself to learn and grow from the differences that present themselves.

Honorable fighting does not **ever** include physical clashes, cruel personal criticism, name calling, the silent treatment, constant nagging or any other forms of abuse. Fighting honorably is when you argue about individual differences constructively and learn something which brings you and your partner closer together. Fighting honorably involves compromise and ends with a solution with which you both feel comfortable. It is not about hurting each other's feelings or tearing each other down. It is about loving yourself and loving your partner enough to want to understand each other and to be understood by each other. It is about honoring differences, but still being heard. This chapter is about fighting in such a way so as to create constructive resolutions.

HOW DO WE DEAL WITH ANGER?

Angry feelings can result from a number of causes. If you feel your partner has taken advantage of you, humiliated you, unfairly criticized you, manipulated you, etc., you would probably feel angry. Should you allow yourself to feel that anger? If that's what you feel, then feel it. What do you do with the feelings? Since angry feelings don't just vanish on their own, it's best to just confront them face-to-face. Will expressing anger to your partner ruin your relationship? Probably not. Actually, you run the best risk of destroying your relationship when you attempt to conceal your anger from your partner because it will surface sooner or later in one form or another. Angry feelings might change into a hidden or underlying issue, which clouds the real problem. If not confronted squarely, anger will fester and get real nasty when it eventually emerges.

Very often we are afraid to express anger because we're not sure how our lover will react to a criticism, or because doing so seems to reflect badly on our partner and/or the relationship. To put it simply, we are afraid to express anger for fear that it will be misinterpreted as lack of love. But that is an unfounded fear, since we have all experienced anger and love at the same time. In order to attain genuine intimacy, disagreeing and making up are essential. It simply says, "We disagree, and we're not perfect, but we still love each other." What is important is to communicate and understand what your anger is about, and whether it is justified or not.

Sylvia, a fairly new member of the lesbian community, participated in one of our PLA workshops on conflict resolution. During one of the group discussions, Sylvia harshly blasted her new partner in life, Gina, and their new relationship because of the occasional arguments that would pop up between the two of them. Gina claimed that Sylvia would avoid conflict at all costs even if it meant lying to her or concealing information from her. Sylvia put the blame for all of their squabbles squarely on Gina's shoulders; after all, she and her former partner — her only previous partner, who happened to be her husband — had never (yes, that's the word she used) had an argument in their seventeen years together. The irony of that statement was obvious to everyone. Clearly, *not* arguing and expressing anger were *not* the key to a happy relationship!

Don't Avoid Conflict.
See It As an Opportunity
to Learn and Grow.

There are some fights that are not worth fighting at all. Most of us have been there before. Have you ever had a quarrel with you lover and, later in the day, not been able to remember what the quarrel was about? Worse yet, have you ever had a quarrel and, after about three hours, not been able to remember what it was about? Many of the arguments couples engage in are over incredibly insignificant issues. If these arguments were fought over important issues that could be resolved, there'd be some redemption in it; but, for the most part, they're not and that's a shame. Think about this when you get into your next argument. When you realize how trivial the subject of your argument is, stop it! If possible, laugh about the ludicrous nature of those trivial arguments before they get out of hand. Consider also that the seemingly insignificant issues over which you argue may really be about something else. Be aware of the hidden issues.

Many petty arguments erupt over bigger issues, more complicated issues. You might feel uncomfortable dealing with specific issues that strike deeply within you and upset you; therefore, you might find something unimportant and attack there. Stephanie, a PLA workshop participant, told about a personal incident where she blasted her partner Mae for leaving her wet raincoat on the foyer floor. They argued for almost an hour about the raincoat. Mae explained why it was okay to leave it where she did. Stephanie argued why it wasn't. They went back and forth in this way. A raincoat just doesn't deserve this much time and attention! Once they separated themselves from the raincoat dilemma and were able to laugh about it, Mae and Stephanie realized that something bigger must have been the catalyst for the notorious raincoat incident. Mae encouraged her partner to share her feelings about their relationship. Stephanie was introspective enough to pinpoint her feelings about the relationship in general at that time. It seems Mae was in the middle of training for a state tennis competition, and because so much of her time was spent on this training, Stephanie felt neglected. But since Stephanie thought that her feelings of neglect might make her seem jealous of Mae's success with her tennis team, she latched onto the nearest minor issue. After their discussion, Mae understood Stephanie's feelings, and so they took steps to remedy their **real** dilemma.

After hearing Stephanie and Mae's story, another couple shared an incident that had occurred while they were on a ski trip in Breckenridge, Colorado. The snow on the mountain was breathtaking; the countryside was magnificent. Every aspect of the scene was exhilarating. Nancy and Colleen had spent a lot of money and had travelled a long distance to enjoy this trip they had both anticipated for such a long time. Finally, there they were on the ski lift. And what were they doing on the ride up? They were arguing — with heartfelt conviction — about whether the ability to spell correctly had any relevance to I.Q.! Can you believe it? What were they thinking! They had used an irrelevant issue, a topic far removed from where they were, in order to detract from what should've been a delightful experience.

If you're thinking the argument was really about something other than the obvious Spelling/I.Q. connection, you're probably right. Nancy and Colleen couldn't help but laugh at themselves as they related their story. In retrospect, they were astounded by their own pettiness and wished that they could relive that time in harmony with one another. Since we can't go back and relive, we need to do our best at attaining one glorious minute after another from here on out.

Don't Borrow Worry!

During the course of one of our workshops, someone used the expression, "Don't borrow worry." She said it to another participant who was worrying about a set of circumstances that did not presently exist, probably never would, and could be remedied if they did come to pass. The truth is that people sometimes create turmoil or conflict where there is none; they do, in fact, "borrow worry." They may borrow from the World of What If. "What if you had been five minutes late?" "What if I had made plans for the evening you committed us to the dinner party?" "What if I had needed that money for the rent?" Perhaps turmoil and worry comfort those people who are used to them. Those individuals who thrive on turmoil often distrust loyalty and fear safety. If you're one of those individuals, you might want to work on feeling comfortable with peace. There can certainly be a feeling of excitement without turmoil. Try to direct your energy in that direction. Allow yourself to travel to that sweet place. While you don't want to avoid conflict, you certainly don't want to create it for the sake of creating it. There's no honor in fighting for the sake of fighting. Pick your battles and make sure they are worthwhile.

Exercise #21

Together with your partner, list your three most ridiculous arguments. This particular exercise might be very difficult to do in one sitting. You may have to come back to it. Perhaps you'll only be able to think of one argument now; but next week you'll be driving in the car, perhaps, and suddenly you'll think, "Oh, yeah, what about the time we argued about...?" Come back to this exercise then.

1. _____

   _____

2. _____

   _____

3. _____

Let Go of the Trivial
and
Focus on the Significant

Since alcohol and certain leisure-type drugs (e.g., marijuana) can play a somewhat relevant role in the social scene for many adults — straight, gay, and lesbian — these substances could possibly cause some serious problems within the relationship. Using these substances could cloud your thoughts, alter your usual mood, distort your perceptions, and lead to some major conflicts between you and your partner. Do you and your lover consistently get into arguments after spending an evening drinking or after smoking marijuana? While many couples say that alcohol and marijuana enhance their fun and pleasure, others state that the use of these substances sometimes leads to inappropriate actions, to suspicious and paranoid behavior, and, ultimately, to some pretty serious arguments.

Exercise #22

Together with your partner, discuss the following questions:.
1. Have alcohol or drugs ever caused problems within your relationship?

If one of you thinks that they have caused problems, then the collective answer is "Yes." If both of you agree that alcohol and drugs have never impacted your relationship, you might consider skipping the rest of the questions and move beyond this exercise.

2. Have either of you said or done anything while under the influence of alcohol or drugs that might have damaged your relationship? (Consider these behaviors: flirting, kissing or having sex with another woman; making unusually hurtful comments either in front of others or privately; behaving in a physically harsh way.)

3. How often have alcohol or drugs negatively impacted your relationship?

4. Would you be willing to refrain from using alcohol and/or drugs if doing so would improve your relationship?

If alcohol and/or drugs are damaging your relationship and if you can't resolve the problem together, seek outside help. It's out there. Refer to your phone directory under Alcohol Abuse, or call your local feminist or gay/lesbian bookstore. Depending on where you live, you may be able to find a gay/lesbian AA group. Don't let alcohol or drugs dictate the terms of your relationship. Fix the problem before any permanent damage is done to yourselves or the relationship.

PUTTING DEFENSES DOWN
BEFORE THE FIGHT BEGINS

When confronted with an imminent argument, what would happen if you dropped your defenses and actually tried to give your partner a solution to the problem before the argument occurred? Imagine this scene: Your partner accuses you of something, and you don't defend yourself. Would you be willing to let your guard down in order to ward off the offense? What's the worst that could happen to you by not defending yourself against your partner's accusations? Consider the following three scenarios and how the battle cry is drowned out by calmness and understanding. (To avoid confusion, we will use Partner C and D so that you'll know we're not talking about you or your partner as Partner A or B.)

Case #1

Partner C: "I thought you said you would do the dishes before I came home from work. I hate when the house is a mess when I come home."

Partner D: "You're right. Sorry. Give me ten minutes and I'll have the dishes done."

Case #2

Partner D: "Why didn't you tell me that Ann and Dawn are coming over tomorrow night? It annoys me when you make plans without telling me."

Partner C: "I'm sorry. I thought I did tell you. If tomorrow's not a good night for you, I'll call Ann and Dawn and set it up for some other time. Not a problem."

Case #3

Partner C: "Well, I just went to get some milk from the refrigerator and the carton is empty. Why do you always take the last of something and just leave the container sitting there? Throw it away and write on the grocery list that we need whatever it is you've used up."

Partner D: "I mustn't have been thinking. Sorry for my inconsiderateness. I'll run
to the grocery and get some more milk. I'm really sorry and I promise
that I'll be more conscious of leaving empty containers in the future."

Loving Allies, Not Enemies

By seeing your partner's point of view, you defuse the situation. It's when you insist
that you've done nothing wrong and that your partner is neurotic for feeling
aggravated that arguments erupt. This is not to say that you should apologize for
something about which you have strong feelings, or for something that you didn't
do. Nor is it to say that you should avoid expressing important feelings because of
fear of conflict. There are times, however, when minor irritations emerge. It is at
these times that you might want to just take a step back and ask yourself, "Is this
battle worthwhile?" There's an alternative. Instead of trying to win meaningless
battles with your partner, do what you can to avoid the trivial spats. Another way to
defuse potentially volatile situations is by keeping a sense of humor. Remember, you
and your partner are loving allies, not enemies!

Once in Battle

There are different techniques you may want to employ once you're in battle with
your partner. Although the desired approach once in battle is to attempt to settle the
issue in question without having a winner and a loser, we often get tangled up in
being right! That becomes the only thing that matters! First of all, the need to win
the arguments has to be replaced with the need for the relationship to grow as a
result of dealing with conflicting feelings or ideas. Have you ever been in an
argument where you and your partner state everything you have to say about the
issue and then state it again and then, perhaps with a slight variation, state it again?
It's all in an attempt to be in the right and to show that your partner is in the wrong.
Stating your case over and over can either be an attempt at making sure you're being
heard or an attempt to wear down your partner to the point that she concedes that
you are absolutely the victor. Instead of arguing to prove your "rightness" and your
partner's "wrongness," try to figure out how to end the argument with a sound
solution for the problem at hand. Try to work things out so that you both win!

10 RULES FOR THE HONORABLE FIGHT

#1

Think about why you're really upset before bringing it up to your partner. Zero in on the real issue. Could something other than the issue you have in mind be causing your anger? Maybe you're annoyed because of a hectic work schedule or because you did not get enough sleep the night before, or perhaps you're upset over a friend's illness? Also, weed out past grievances and focus on the immediate cause of your displeasure.

It's important at this juncture to be very honest. Maybe you're upset with your partner for "flirting" with the new woman who just moved in next door, but you feel too embarrassed or proud to verbalize that feeling. Instead, you might attack your partner on an issue that is safer for you — "Why do you always try to impress people? It makes you seem so insecure." This way, you don't have to admit that you feel jealous of what you perceived to be her flirting with the neighbor. You've set it up so that your partner might feel the need to defend her sense of security instead of you, perhaps, having to defend your own. Unfortunately, the true issue is lost. Not only is trying to resolve the wrong conflict a total waste of time, the true source of conflict remains unresolved. And you can be sure it will resurface!

#2

Keep your arguments focused on the issue at hand. You might even try setting a time limit of 20 minutes on discussing the disagreement. Both of you can usually express all of your feelings on an issue, along with possible solutions, in this amount of time. You don't want to get sucked into **The Dreaded Fight With No End,** the fight that goes through the repetitive cycle of stating and restating positions. A time limit that you can both agree upon may help alleviate useless repetition. After an honest attempt at coming up with workable solutions to the problem, learn to forgive and let go of any negative feelings associated with the problem.

#3

Be completely attentive to what your partner is saying. Instead of thinking about what you will say next in defense of yourself or about what you can perhaps retrieve from the past to show that she's been guilty of the same offense or worse, really listen to what is being said. If she's complaining to you about coming home late, listen to her concerns. Was she worried about your safety? Was she fearful of infidelity? Was she jealous that you were out and she was stuck home? Was she just wishing you had phoned home to check in? Instead of addressing what our partners are actually saying, we may immediately launch into a defense of why we were right. By repeating what your partner has said, you may grasp a better understanding of her feelings and you may indirectly help her clarify her real concerns.

#4

Avoid generalizations. Steer clear of statements like, "You **never** pick up your clothes" or, "You're **always** late." Again, just as when there is blaming and criticizing, you end up with a partner who's focused on the times she **did** pick up her clothes and those times she **did** get ready or arrive on time. Negotiation, compromise, or any other possible solution to repair the problem is lost. The focus is shifted. It's important to present the specific problem to your partner if you want a resolution.

#5

Pick an appropriate time to air your grievance. Pick a time when you can express yourself clearly and calmly and when your partner has the opportunity to carefully listen and respond to the issue you have presented. As one of you is walking out of the door to go to work or while you're both enjoying yourselves at a party, for example, are not good times to deal with the grievance. If the issue is important to you and the time never seems to be right, set up a date to have your fight.
If you're doing something that really isn't so important and you can give your partner the opportunity to say what is on her mind, do it. Don't ignore her, for example, by continuing to watch TV or read a book when she is trying to tell you something that is important to her. Give her your full attention.

Some relationship experts say that couples should never go to bed angry. There are times when it is a good idea to do just that and then wake up the next morning to a new day and a new attitude. Many petty arguments that occur late in the evening occur simply because you are cross (either one or both of you) and need some sleep. The upset feelings frequently dissolve into Dreamland during the course of the night, never to be felt or brought to mind again. If the feelings haven't dissolved during the course of the night, however, perhaps in the morning you'll at least have a different and more favorable perspective on the problem.

#6

Tell your partner about how you feel without blaming or criticizing her. Avoid statements like, "You are such a slob" or, "You just can't be trusted to be on time." As soon as you blame or criticize your partner, you're setting her up to defend herself. Once your partner starts defending herself, any negotiation, compromise, or any other solution to repair the problem is put on the back burner and the focus is lost. Every now and then during your argument, use terms of endearment that you usually call your partner to let her know that you still love her although you have a problem with a particular issue inside the relationship. Don't, however, use the terms in a condescending way. Even the use of your partner's first name during an argument can provide each of you with a sense of safety and love. Notice that the more tenderness you put into the fight, the more you get back and the sooner the conflict can be resolved.

#7

Keep your arguments safe. Abandoning the relationship because of a problem should not be presented as a solution; therefore, avoid phrases like, "If you don't like it, leave."; "You are so disgusting. Why don't you just pack your crap and go?"; or, "I'll just have to find somebody else to give me what you won't." Being hurtful and threatening does nothing to solve conflict. Similarly, **never ever ever** name-call your lover. Never fling out insulting tags such as "stupid" or "idiot" or "pig" or "creep." You may recognize these tags better in context; for example, "Only an idiot would think that," or, "You're such a pig when it comes to keeping this house clean." If you have ever used any name-calling tags or if you ever do, you need to stop and ask yourself this key question, "What does that kind of name-calling say about me as a person?" Out of all of the lesbians in the world, you consciously chose and committed yourself to this one. Why would you have chosen a relationship with, and committed to, an "idiot," a "pig," or often worse? Why would you want to stay in a relationship with her? More importantly, why would she want to stay in a relationship where you think so ill of her?

Don't make fun of your partner's opinions or shortcomings. If you have any regard for yourself at all, never do this in front of other people. Hurting a person's feelings destroys her self-esteem. Have you ever felt more loving toward someone as a result of being mocked by them? Mocking your lover is a sign of weakness; it also strips your nest of its safety and serenity.

Similarly, don't criticize your lover's family unfairly, no matter what you think of them. Even when your partner criticizes her family (e.g., if she says, "My father is a real loser,") don't add to it by saying, "So is your mother."

Remember, the goal is not to have a personal victory over your partner. A triumph for just one of you is a lot like a failure. The only victory is a victory for the relationship!

#8

Keep your conflict statements "I" centered. When faced with a confrontation, try starting all of your sentences off with "I" and then give a reason for your feelings; for example, "I feel upset when I come home from work and your clothes are all over the floor. I can't relax when the house is a mess," or, "I thought you promised that you'd be ready for the dinner party at 6:00. I feel uncomfortable walking into a dinner party an hour late." Of course there are several ways these lines can be delivered. It's up to you to present them as calmly and as lovingly as you want them to be resolved. You are assuming ownership of your feelings and stating why you would like the situation resolved. You and your partner are then in a fair place to start fixing the problem.

#9

Don't involve other people in your arguments or problems. You especially do not want to do this if the involvement would embarrass or upset your partner in any way. If you have a spat, work it out privately. The only exception should be if you are involved in couple therapy or perhaps are discussing the problem with a close friend whom you both trust. When you include other people in your fights, especially mutual friends and family members, you're creating a monster. Remember: What lovers can forgive, others may not. If you as an individual feel you must air certain issues concerning your relationship with someone, only share this sensitive information with your therapist, if you have one, or with an open-minded friend who is your friend separate from your relationship. In any case, don't come back to your partner and say, "My therapist (or my friend at work) says that you were wrong about (whatever it is that is causing the problem)." That's an unfair stance that can only cause frustration for your partner.

#10

Offer one or more possible solutions. After presenting the problem as you perceive it, offer one or more solutions to fix the problem and give your partner the chance to do the same. This allows your partner to see that what you're presenting is reasonable and that you're willing to be flexible with how the dilemma is resolved. It also helps to take blame out of the situation. Employ the problem-solving formula given in the next chapter.

You'll notice that the ten rules for honorable fighting often overlap each other. Study the rules together and make a commitment to one another to stick to the rules in order to **turn your conflicts into avenues of growth**.

If you find that nagging behavior has become a habit in your relationship, break the cycle immediately. The nagging can be directed at something as small as your partner leaving the cap off the toothpaste tube or accidentally throwing out this week's *TV Guide*. Nagging has no place in a relationship where partners respect one another as equals.

Word to the Wise:
Learn To Admit When you're wrong.
Apologize!

RECAP OF THE 10 RULES OF HONORABLE FIGHTING

1. Make sure you're clear about what is really bothering you.

2. Focus on the precise topic of your argument.

3. Listen attentively to what is being said.

4. Avoid generalizations.

5. Pick an appropriate time to air your grievances.

6. Say how you feel without blaming or criticizing.

7. Maintain argument safety by banning all threatening or name-calling tactics.

8. Keep your conflict statements "I" centered.

9. Don't involve other people in your arguments.

10. Offer one or more solutions to resolve the conflict.

Exercise #23

Together, as a couple, record the subject of your next two arguments — one on this page, the second on the next. That's right! Remind each other that you need to come back to this page and actually write down the topics of your arguments. Be sure to write down which of the "10 Rules of Honorable Fighting" either of you was conscious of using.

Argument X:

1. General Topic of Argument:

_____

_____

2. Rules of Honorable Fighting Used:

_____

_____

3. How Was This Argument Resolved?

_____

_____

Comments: ✍

Exercise #23 (Continued)

Together, as a couple, record the subject of your second argument. That's right! Remind each other that you need to come back to this page and actually write down the topic of a second argument. Remember to write down which of the "10 Rules of Honorable Fighting" either of you was conscious of using.

Argument Y:

1. General Topic of Argument:

_____

_____

2. Rules of Honorable Fighting Used:

_____

_____

3. How Was This Argument Resolved?

_____

_____

More pages are provided for this exercise in Appendix C and D.

Comments: ✍

PRODUCTIVE ALTERNATIVES TO THE ROUTINE ARGUMENT

Besides using the ten rules for honorable fighting, you may want to consider the following creative argument suggestions:

1. **Letter Writing** - For some people, it is difficult to vocally express thoughts and feelings. If there is an issue that you would like to present but find it difficult to express face-to-face, try writing a letter to your lover. When you write a letter, you can present everything you want to say with time to organize your thoughts for a concise and unemotional presentation and without interruption from your lover during that presentation. When your partner reads about whatever it is that is upsetting you, she might not feel so defensive, especially if you add assurances of love and possible solutions to the problem within the letter.

2. **Switching Sides** - After both of you have had your say in an argument and tension or anger still exists, force yourselves to switch sides and take your partner's position in the argument. This may be hard to do because of the emotional nature of most arguments, but try it. When each of you sincerely attempts to express what your partner is feeling and thinking, it will help both of you see the other's side of things. If switching sides causes laughter and nothing more, that's not such a bad result either.

3. **Notebook Nagging** - Keep a notebook on a desk, bookshelf, or some other central location. Mark one side of the notebook cover "NAGGING" and the other side "PRAISING." When your lover does something that is relatively minor but you still feel the need to gripe about it, write your complaint in the nagging section. Here's the catch — for every gripe you make, you have to record words of praise in the other section of the notebook. If you don't feel like taking the time to write the complaint down in the notebook, maybe it's not worth mentioning in the first place.

Exercise #24

Together, formulate one additional alternative to the traditional argument. Your plans can even be a variation of letter writing, switching sides, or notebook nagging. Keep the 10 Rules of Honorable Fighting in mind. Perhaps post them on your refrigerator. Destructive behavior such as physical violence, verbal abuse, or the silent treatment is banned from consideration. See Appendix E and F.

A Key Thought: Harmony and Love Lead to Shorter Arguments

The more harmony and love you can create within your relationship, the shorter and more productive your arguments will be. So if shorter and more productive arguments appeal to you, consciously work on the harmony and love within your relationship. There's a predictable balance in all of this which will hopefully leave the two of you with more time to enjoy one another.

 6

PROBLEM-SOLVE AS A COUPLE

In most relationships, there are one or two troublesome issues that crop up on a regular basis and never seem to go away. Although the issues often deal with money or jealousies, they are not confined to these subjects. Whatever the issue, if it is not examined and resolved, it will continually pop up and cause problems in your relationship. You have a choice to either slam the doors shut or throw the doors wide open when dealing with these issues. If you and your partner want a healthy and loving relationship, throw the doors open to problems in such a way that your relationship will grow. Effective problem-solving is the most constructive way to open those doors to the issues that separate you. It is in this way that the two of you can come together as a team to lovingly address the issues. This does not mean that you should "borrow trouble" or create problems where there aren't any. This chapter presents a formula for couples to deal rationally and fairly with those perplexing and annoying problems that inevitably arise in most relationships.

Before you do any exercises, consider the following problem and formula for remedying the problem.

Problem: Stella is excited about an international ballet company which will be performing in her town soon. When she tells her lover Michelle about the performance, Michelle lets Stella know in no uncertain terms that she is bored by ballet and does not want to go. Stella feels frustrated and disappointed.

What are Stella's options at this point? In order to get Michelle to change her mind, Stella could beg and cry or rage and pout. If she does, she may really get what she wants...and some things she doesn't. She may get to go to the ballet, but it will be with someone who not only feels bored, but is also resentful. Does that sound like a good time to you?

Because we all differ in interests, opinions, and needs, it is important to respect the differences. Stella and Michelle are two separate women, with different interests, opinions and needs. They don't both have to like the ballet!

BASIC FORMULA FOR PROBLEM-SOLVING

1. Determine the specific problem.
2. Come up with five possible solutions to correct the problem.
3. Select the two most usable solutions out of the five.
4. Weigh the advantages and disadvantages of both usable solutions.
5. Decide which of the two choices is most comfortable or reasonable for you.

How it Works:

Define the Problem:
Stella knows what the problem is; she wants to go to the ballet and Michelle does not. She therefore has to come up with some possible solutions for her problem, either with Michelle's help or without it. After some thought, Stella comes up with the following list of solutions:

Possible Solutions:
1. Break up with Michelle and get another date to take her to the ballet.
2. Go with a family member or a friend.
3. Promise Michelle that if she goes with her, Stella will gladly go with her to the upcoming softball tournament.
4. Go alone to the ballet.
5. Don't go at all.

Once Stella comes up with her possible solutions, she must decide on the top two. In this case, she selects Solutions #2 and #4. She decides on the possible advantages and disadvantages for both solutions. Stella doesn't like traveling to the city at night by herself, and she would enjoy the ballet more with another person; therefore, she decides on Solution #2 and decides to call a friend to go with her. If she cannot find a friend to go with her, Stella resolves that she will go alone to see the ballet.

When You're Confused, Try to See It Her Way

Another situation that called for the problem-solving formula involved Chris and Peggy, a couple who have had very few serious issues that presented any threat to their relationship during the past decade. Recently, though, Chris and Peggy were planning to celebrate their tenth anniversary together, when they realized that they had quite different views on how to celebrate the occasion. Chris envisioned a large extravaganza. Many friends and family members would be invited. A minister would preside over a formal ceremony. A caterer would provide food and drink. A three-piece classical ensemble would play ethereal, romantic music. She also envisioned Peggy having the same expectation for the anniversary celebration as she did. Chris not only wanted Peggy to be just as excited about her plans as she was, she also wanted Peggy to help prepare for the celebration with the same enthusiasm she felt.

When Chris came to the realization that Peggy was not interested in helping with preparations and that she was feeling distressed over the whole affair, Chris felt frustrated, angry and afraid. Why was Peggy trying to ruin the day that she had planned so carefully and excitedly? Why was Peggy being so uncooperative? Was Peggy dissatisfied with the relationship itself, perhaps reconsidering the whole ten years together, and not interested in celebrating the event at all?

When Chris and Peggy finally decided to discuss and solve their problem, they employed the formula presented earlier. Chris stated her problem with Peggy's disinterest in the anniversary plans. Peggy stated her problem, which Chris was truly hearing for the first time. Peggy had wanted them to spend a romantic week at a mountain chalet to celebrate their tenth anniversary. She hadn't said how she felt before because Chris seemed so swept up with the planning of the anniversary ceremony, plans that Peggy felt had nothing to do with her or what she wanted. Both of them knew that financially, they couldn't afford to have a huge ceremony **and** go to the mountain chalet. Chris and Peggy proceeded to list possible ways to settle their dilemma. They came up with the following solutions:

1. Chris can go to the anniversary ceremony; Peggy can go to the mountains. (They were both still a bit annoyed with each other at this point.)
2. They would have the anniversary ceremony just as Chris had planned, and they would not go to the mountains.
3. They would go to the mountains and not have the ceremony at all.
4. They would have a much smaller anniversary ceremony without a caterer or the three-piece classical ensemble, and they would go to the mountains for four days instead of seven.
5. They would have the anniversary ceremony as Chris had planned, and then in six months go to the mountain chalet to celebrate their anniversary again.

Chris and Peggy agreed that Solutions #4 and 5 were the best. They discussed the pros and cons of each and decided on Solution #4. They also decided that in the future they would discuss in advance what each person's preference was for celebrating a given occasion. Their communication would be clearer.

The Key Ingredient to Understanding Is Clear Communication

You and your partner will now have the opportunity to solve two problem areas in your relationship. Although there is only space for two problems in the *Feathering Your Nest* exercise, you can repeat the same steps for an endless number of dilemmas on the blank pages of the "Personal Notes" section near the end of the book.

Exercise #25-A

Name_____

Separately from your partner, state two problems that seem to come up with some frequency in your relationship. In the blank provided, check the one problem that is more important to you, and circle the appropriate answer.

Problem A:

_____

_____

Can this problem be resolved reasonably?   No   Yes   Not Sure

Would you be willing to change some aspect
    of your own behavior to resolve
    the problem?   No   Yes   Not Sure

If yes, what behavior could you change?

_____

If no, why?

_____

Have you and your partner ever seriously
    tried to resolve this problem?   No   Yes   Not Sure

(Exercise 25-A continued)

Would your relationship be happier if this
issue were resolved?   No   Yes   Not Sure

Problem B:

_____

_____

Can this problem be resolved reasonably?   No   Yes   Not Sure

Would you be willing to change some aspect
of your own behavior to resolve the
problem?   No   Yes   Not Sure

If yes, what behavior could you change?

_____

If no, why?

_____

Have you and your partner ever seriously
tried to resolve this problem?   No   Yes   Not Sure

Would your relationship be happier if this
issue were resolved?   No   Yes   Not Sure

**Partner A: Do not proceed to the next page;
Exercise #25-B is for your partner to complete.**

Exercise #25-B

Name_____

Separately from your partner, state two problems that seem to come up with some frequency in your relationship. In the blank provided, check the one problem that is more important to you and circle the appropriate response.

Problem A:

_____

_____

Can this problem be resolved reasonably?	No	Yes	Not Sure
Would you be willing to change some aspect of your own behavior to resolve the problem?	No	Yes	Not Sure

If yes, what behavior could you change?

_____

If no, why?

_____

Have you and your partner ever seriously tried to resolve this problem?	No	Yes	Not Sure
Would your relationship be happier if this issue were resolved?	No	Yes	Not Sure

Problem B:

_____

_____

Can this problem be resolved reasonably?   No   Yes   Not Sure
Would you be willing to change some aspect
    of your own behavior to resolve
    the problem?   No   Yes   Not Sure

If yes, what behavior could you change?

_____

If no, why?

_____

Have you and your partner ever seriously
    tried to resolve this problem?   No   Yes   Not Sure

Would your relationship be happier if this
    issue were resolved?   No   Yes   Not Sure

Once you are each finished stating your two problems and answering the questions that follow, come together again. Especially for this exercise, try to pick a time when both of you are feeling loving, positive and creative. Together, see if any issue is repeated in the other's list. Keep in mind that you and your lover are in a position of power; you have the ability to change things for the better. It's in your hands.

Examine the problems carefully. Together, discuss the answers to the questions that each of you were earlier asked to consider individually:

1. Can the problems be reasonably resolved? _____

2. Would each of you be willing to change some aspect of your own behavior to help resolve the problems? _____

3. Have the two of you ever sat down and tried to rationally and fairly come up with real solutions to the problems? _____

4. Would your relationship be happier and healthier if the problems were settled and removed from your lives? _____

5. Are you both willing to work on the problem in a serious and constructive way? _____

After taking yourselves through the process of effective problem-solving, hopefully you are both able to see how the technique can be a source of learning and growth for you as a couple and individually. Solving problems fairly and lovingly is a positive way to reinforce the bond between you.

Working Together, You Can Overcome All Obstacles!

Exercise #26

Together, select the most bothersome recurring problem from Exercise #25. Select one that you both agree can be resolved rationally and fairly. Follow through using the basic formula for problem-solving outlined earlier in the chapter.

1. Problem:

_____

_____

_____

2. Possible Solutions: (If you can think of more than five, write them in the side margins. Too many solutions is never a problem.)

1._____

2._____

3._____

4._____

5._____

3. Put a check next to two of the most usable solutions written under "Possible Solutions."

4. Together, discuss which of the two solutions is better for your situation and why. Write it in the space below: ✍

_____

_____

_____

5. Now answer the following questions:

1. Are you both comfortable with the solution selected?   Yes   No   Not Sure

2. What, if any, special preparation would it take to put
    the solution into effect?

_____

_____

3. Are you both ready to put the solution into effect?   Yes   No   Not Sure

4. Will your relationship be happier and healthier once
    this problem is resolved?   Yes   No   Not Sure

You may be thinking, "As if I'm going to solve all of the problems in my relationship by going through all these steps!" Of course you won't. Your life would come to a dead standstill. Most small or temporary problems require quick on-the-spot solutions. There will be times, however, that "going through all these steps" will actually be timesaving rather than time-consuming; after all, going through the steps in a purposeful, sane manner might very well prevent an argument that lasts for hours or days, or, for that matter, the entire span of your relationship.

Problems That Aren't Your Problem

There are some problems that you should accept as being beyond your ability to solve. What if your lover's parents cannot stand you because you're a lesbian? What if they don't want any such "pervert" to visit their home or to even hear your name mentioned? (Of course, if they knew you, they'd be crazy about you; but their prejudice keeps them from absolutely loving you and from wanting you to visit.) You wrote them a letter letting them know that you adore their daughter, that you have heard wonderful things about them as parents and that you would love to meet them. They tore the letter into pieces as soon as they saw that it was from you. In all likelihood, there is nothing you can do to change their minds about their pre-conception of you. They're miserably comfortable in their homophobia and homohatred. There's nothing you can do to solve this problem.

Friends may say that pushing your partner to cut her parents off from her life might bring them to their senses. It may or may not. That's your partner's decision. You might tell your partner how the situation makes you feel; but restrain yourself from pushing her into doing anything that she doesn't feel comfortable doing. If there is a chasm that develops between child and parents, let it be between them. If your lover asks for your feelings or opinions on the issue, of course, be honest; but try not to be too harsh or pushy in this area. This particular problem, although it may rile you up emotionally, has nothing to do with you in actuality. Back away from it. Don't waste valuable time arguing with your lover over the issue and don't take responsibility for her parents' ignorance.

Problems That Have No Solution

It's important to acknowledge that some problems that arise in the relationship have no solution. For example, if neatness is not an issue with your partner, yet is crucial to you, you may just have to compromise and let it go at that. You may spend much of your time together trying to get your partner to see the evil of her untidy ways; but much valuable time is lost in the interim. Remember: You and your partner are not the same person; you're two different people with different personalities! If you truly can't stand messiness, why did you commit to this person in the first place? If it wasn't so important then, why is it so important now?

You probably won't be able to change your partner, but some compromise might be possible. If your partner refuses to put away her clothes upon undressing, but instead leaves shirts and pants and socks and underwear all over the house, perhaps you can work out an arrangement where one room in the house (preferably one where guests don't venture) becomes the designated clothes catcher. Brainstorm ways that each of you can give a little on the issue. You may not be able to solve the problem completely, but you can definitely come up with a mutual compromise. Ultimately, you need to ask yourself, "Do I want to end the relationship over this issue, or can I learn to accept this problem and live with it?"

Use the problem-solving format given earlier in this chapter and creatively solve or compromise where you can. If you and your partner cannot solve the problem or find a compromise to reasonably satisfy you, either end the relationship or accept the differences, or seek professional counseling. Don't spend your lives bickering over differences that won't go away. Life is too short to be miserable about what you can't change.

Problems That Can Be Solved

Most problems that weigh heavily upon relationships *are* solvable. Try applying the problem-solving formula recapped at the end of this chapter to those areas of conflict that seem to surface again and again in your relationship. Although you have to spend some time and thought-energy going through the process, it could save your relationship! Going through this simple but effective process can not only strengthen your relationship, it can give both of you powerful tools with which to handle the curve balls that life will inevitably throw your way.

RECAP OF THE FORMULA FOR PROBLEM-SOLVING:

1. Determine the specific problem.
2. Come up with five possible solutions.
3. Select two of the best solutions.
4. Weigh the advantages and disadvantages.
5. Pick the better of the two choices.

FAN THE FLAMES OF ROMANCE

According to a Positive Living Alliance (PLA) survey completed by lesbians throughout the United States, there are many different concepts of what it means to be "romantic." What is romantic to one person may not be romantic to another. So before you go about the delicious task of creating romance, know what it means to be "romantic" in your lover's mind and in your own.

Exercise #27-A

Name_____

Separately from your partner, complete the following statement and take as much space as you need:

I am being romantic when I... ✍

Exercise #27-B

Name_____

Separately from your partner, complete the following statement and take as much space as you need:

> **I am being romantic when I...** ✍

Exercise #28

After you and your lover have separately completed the statement "I am being romantic when I...," come back together, discuss your answers, and come up with a mutual definition of what it means to be "romantic."

> **Our couple definition of what it means to be "romantic":** ✍

For Your Information!

As mentioned earlier, lesbians throughout the United States were asked to respond to the following question: **I am being romantic when I _____.** The general trend of their answers clustered around the sentiments expressed in the following three responses:

1. "I am being romantic when I express a physical and/or emotional attraction to another person."

2. "I am being romantic when I send a message — usually a subtle message — that says, 'You are the special love of my life.'"

3. "I am being romantic when I act in a way to get a sexual response."

Exercise #29

Together, list the three most romantic memories of your relationship. (If you can think of more, don't hold back; continue a longer list in the side margins or in the "Personal Notes" section at the back of *Feathering Your Nest.*)   ✍

1.

2.

3.

When you're being romantic, you're celebrating the intimacy of the relationship that you both treasure. You're letting your partner know — either through words or actions — that she is loved and valued. It is usually the acts of love, rather than the words of love, that present the most convincing statement of genuine affection. Since we don't all have the time to sit around gazing into our lover's eyes and whispering our sweet sentiments, you might want to expand your definition of romance to include what you do in daily living, what you extend to each other ordinarily in the areas of care and devotion. Daily living can be filled with expressions of love and can be much more meaningful and convincing than the gazes or the whispers. In this way, you can make romance a daily part of your lives.

Don't think for a second that small expressions of love can't make an immense difference in your relationship. Doing nice things is contagious. Watch what happens when you put some of these suggestions into action. Below is a list of fifty gestures that can stimulate an abundance of romance in your relationship. Place a check ✔ next to the expressions that you would like to consider.

50 EXPRESSIONS OF LOVE

❒ 1. Write a love letter or poem to your partner telling her how much you love her, how attractive you think she is, and what impact she has had on your life. Put it in her lunch sack, on the front seat of the car, in a book she is reading, or on her pillow.

❒ 2. Leave a brief note on the bathroom mirror telling her how sexy she was the night before.

❒ 3. If it's your lover's turn to do the mundane task of cleaning the kitchen after a meal, insist on taking her turn while she relaxes.

❒ 4. Have a warm bubble bath set up for your lover. Light a few candles in the bathroom and lay out clean towels, talcum powder, and a cuddly pair of pajamas. Have the sound of Mozart or Vivaldi wafting in softly from a nearby room.

❏ 5. Massage your lover's feet or back or neck or hands while you lounge around together.

❏ 6. Surprise her with tickets to a play, movie, or art exhibit she's been dying to see.

❏ 7. After serving a surprise breakfast in bed, make love to her.

❏ 8. In front of other people, compliment your lover. You don't have fawn to over each other, but a simple "I love that outfit on you" or "The color of yourhair is so pretty in the sunlight" would be nice.

❏ 9. Never forget her birthday, your first-date anniversary, your move-in-together anniversary, etc.

❏ 10. When the two of you are working together in the kitchen, play one of your favorite slow songs on the stereo and ask your lover to dance with you.

❏ 11. Kiss her behind the neck while she's reading or cooking or watching TV.

❏ 12. Tell your lover how smart you think she is.

❏ 13. The next time the two of you have an argument, force yourself to see her point of view and give in to her. (This is probably the greatest expression of love. It is definitely one of the most difficult.)

❏ 14. Do a task for your lover that she has talked about doing (e.g., wash the car, iron pants) but has been dreading.

❏ 15. Take your lover to an outdoor concert or just a private little picnic for the two of you. Pack a blanket, a good bottle of wine, candles, cheese, and bread or crackers. Don't forget matches and a corkscrew.

❏ 16. Hold her hand as you walk down a nature trail or, if you feel safe and comfortable, as you walk down a city street.

17. While she is driving and without being too distracting, gently play with the hair on or near the back of her neck.

18. After making love, gently wipe her genital area with a warm (not hot) cloth.

19. Surprise her by cooking her favorite meal and having it ready when she gets home from work. Serve up a glass of fine wine.

20. Pick up a movie from the video store and her favorite takeout meal.

21. Send her flowers at work and sign it "From the one who adores you," "I feel so lucky," or with any other loving message.

22. When she is feeling down, lend an attentive ear and a strong shoulder.

23. When you go shopping without her, bring her back a surprise (e.g., a new sweater, a book or CD she's been wanting to buy, massage oil).

24. When your partner is leaving to go somewhere in a car, kiss her and remind her to buckle up the seatbelt.

25. Drink champagne on a park bench either early in the morning or at dusk. (Don't drive after drinking and don't think you have to finish off the bottle.)

26. If it would be pleasurable for her, invite her family over for a surprise visit and barbecue.

27. Celebrate her victories (e.g., job promotion, a pay raise, new job, graduation).

28. Take her to an elegant restaurant to dine. (Notice that we didn't say "to eat.") Tell your waiter or waitress from the start that you don't want to be rushed. Order one course at a time. Savor each before you order the next. Spend the time in between courses flirting with one another, talking about your favorite romantic experiences **with her**. Make it last at least two hours. Tip your waiter or waitress generously.

☐ 29. Go for a walk in the park at dusk and talk about when the two of you first started dating.

☐ 30. Take your partner on a date to some place she has always wanted to go but has never been (e.g., planetarium, winery, horse races).

☐ 31. If it's an appropriate situation, send her mother flowers on your partner's birthday thanking her for raising such a wonderful daughter.

☐ 32. If she has a car and it's the appropriate time, surprise your partner by taking the car to get an oil change, to have the tires and fluid levels checked, and to fill the gas tank.

☐ 33. If she gets a haircut and is feeling downhearted about it, let her know that even if she were bald, you'd think she was beautiful.

☐ 34. Throw a blanket in your backyard and sprawl upon it together for stargazing. Have a plate of easy-to-eat fruit (e.g., strawberries, grapes, sliced apples and oranges) and a couple of different cheeses diced up. A bottle of fine blueberry wine (not the kind with a screw-on top) would also be a nice touch.

☐ 35. Sing to her. Make up your own song or strike up those vocal chords with "Love Will Keep Us Together" or one of your other favorites.

☐ 36. Treat your lover and her mother to Sunday brunch.

☐ 37. Turn all the lights out in your living room, light a few candles, and listen to a Billie Holliday, Mahalia Jackson, Sarah Vaughn or any one of your favorite soulful singers with your lover in your arms.

☐ 38. Throw a surprise party for her birthday.

❑ 39. When she's sick and confined to bed, baby her. Make sure she has water or juice nearby. Keep track of the time she needs to take her medication. Check to see if you can get her anything. Perhaps even sing her a lullaby.

❑ 40. Bring your partner a snack or a drink when she is busy with a task.

❑ 41. Unless she is on a diet or simply watching her weight, give your partner an expensive box of chocolates. (And keep your hands out of it!)

❑ 42. If your partner drinks coffee or tea in the morning, learn how to fix it exactly the way she likes it.

❑ 43. Keep your partner's photo in your wallet.

❑ 44. Hold hands while riding in the car, without risking safety at the wheel.

❑ 45. Surprise her by washing and waxing her car.

❑ 46. Offer to scrub her back while she's bathing.

❑ 47. Flirt with your partner at a party. Whisper in her ear, "I can't wait to be alone with you." Mouth the words, "I love you" or simply wink from across the room.

❑ 48. If you're savoring food after your lover has already gobbled up all of hers, save your last bite for her.

❑ 49. If your partner expresses a desire to see you in silk lingerie or even flannel pajamas, surprise her one night.

❑ 50. Together with your partner, read through *Feathering Your Nest*, responding honestly to the exercises that can strengthen your relationship.

Many of the suggestions listed above may need your personalized touch. If you live in the city and don't have a backyard, for example, you may want to take suggestion #34 and change the locale to your balcony or patio. If you do not drink alcohol, you can omit that element from the suggestions that include it. The suggestions are to enhance **your** relationship, so modify any of the expressions of love to fit your own situation and your own tastes. If the list has done nothing but given you ideas for your own expressions of love, then that's a positive step in the right direction. Many items in the list provide your partner with positive anticipation, which helps keep the passion in relationships. Make a habit of gifting your lover with sincere expressions of your love! You'll be surprised at what comes back to you.

Remember That
What You Do
Says More Than What You Say!

Keep the list handy. Periodically pull an expression of love from the above list or from your own list and use it in your relationship. Create new expressions. All of this is romance! It is the daily love you extend that creates the intimate bonds that will keep you happily together.

Exercise #30

Together with your lover, list five additional expressions of love that would appeal to both of you.

1. _____

2. _____

3. _____

4. _____

5. _____

Be aware that romance can play a key role in all aspects of your life, not just in the bedroom. Many of the lesbians interviewed while we were writing *Feathering Your Nest* said that some of their most romantic moments have occurred outside the bedroom and were, in fact, not even directly sexual in nature. Gentle touching during the course of the day was a highly desirable behavior enjoyed by many. Yes, we all long for, and cherish, those gentle touches and hugs. They reassure us that we are indeed loved! If you're not getting them, ask for them. If you're not giving them, start.

To keep the romance alive, plan for it and make it real. Creating a stable and loving home, sharing interests, being spontaneous, setting goals, communicating openly and attentively, solving problems constructively and fairly, and having fun are all important components of romance. When you feel genuinely good about your partner and yourself, giving unselfishly is easy. Giving unselfishly is a must for true romance.

"To love is to be engaged is to work is to be interested is to create."

— Lina Wertmuller, film director

8

ENJOY THE PLEASURES OF SEX

Most of the lesbians interviewed stated that their best sexual encounters with their partner have occurred during the following times:
1. when they were getting along well in their relationship
   and having fun together;
2. when they were intimate in nonsexual ways; and
3. when they were being productive and satisfied in other
   areas of their lives.

It's difficult for many individuals to engage in sex when other areas of the relationship are shaky. As stated previously, all areas of the relationship are linked together. But if all is well emotionally, you're ready for the pleasures of the flesh.

But What's There To Do?

You can have sex with the lights on or with the lights off, with your clothes on or with your clothes off, with a dildo or vibrator or with your bare hands, with music playing or with no sounds but one another, with a "dirty" mouth or with a sweet one. You can have sex with your tongue or with your toes. You can have sex in the morning, in the afternoon, or at night; in your bedroom, in your backyard, in the shower, in the car, or under the kitchen table. You can have sex at a hotel in town or out of town. You can have sex with the roughness of S & M or the gentleness of kittens. You can have a two-way or a three-way. You can have sex over the phone or live and in person. You can have a quickie or an all-nighter. This is just the beginning of the pleasurable possibilities. Oh, there's a lot to do!

Exercise #31-A

Name_____

Separately from your partner, check ✔ the column that best signifies your answers to the following questions concerning your present sex life:

	Yes	No	Somewhat

1. Are you satisfied with the quality of sex?

2. Are you satisfied with the frequency of sex?

3. Are you comfortable talking to your partner about
    your sexual feelings?

4. Would you like your sexual encounters to have
    more of an element of surprise?

5. Would you like more variety (e.g., technique, setting)?

6. Would you prefer one approach over another
    when your partner initiates sex?

7. Is safe sex a concern for you?

Comments: ✎

Exercise #31-B

Name_____

Separately from your partner, check ✔ the column that best signifies your answers to the following questions concerning your present sex life:

                                                          Yes   No   Somewhat

1. Are you satisfied with the quality of sex?

2. Are you satisfied with the frequency of sex?

3. Are you comfortable talking to your partner about your sexual feelings?

4. Would you like your sexual encounters to have more of an element of surprise?

5. Would you like more variety (i.e. technique, setting)?

6. Would you prefer one approach over another when your partner initiates sex?

7. Is safe sex a concern for you?

After both of you have completed Exercise #31, discuss your answers. Be open to your partner's feelings and thoughts. Be willing to relax and experiment.

TWO REALLY IMPORTANT RULES FOR SEXUAL PLEASURE

➧ 1. Tell or show your partner what feels good to you. Don't expect her to read your mind. Communicate your wishes in a positive and loving way; don't be critical.

+ 2. Focus on sexual pleasure, not performance. Allow yourself to enjoy love making whether it is intense or playful. And don't limit sex to genital gratification. Sexual pleasure can come in the form of a passionate kiss or even a suggestive glance from across a table or room. Eliminate as many of life's noisy distractions (e.g., telephone, television) as possible. Focused enjoyment is the key.

FIVE ACTS
THAT STIMULATE SEXUAL DESIRE

The couples we interviewed were asked to list those actions or situations that increased their sexual desire. Listed below are the top five responses.

+ 1. TALKING ABOUT SEX

Lesbian couples agreed that talking about their actual sexual exploits with each other, especially about first kisses and risky encounters, or fantasy situations (what they would like to happen), is the biggest sexual stimulator. Many couples also revealed that having these conversations in romantic settings, such as while walking in the park, dining in a restaurant, or cuddling in bed, aroused sexual desire.

+ 2. UNUSUAL SETTINGS

Lesbian couples not only found that going out of town and staying in a hotel (thus avoiding the normal distractions of home life) revved up the sex drive — even moving to another section of the house lends a spark (e.g., in front of a blazing fireplace, on the living room sofa, or moving to other interesting places such as the woods alongside a ski run, under a blanket on an airline jet, in your parents' house) frequently provided additional stimulation. You may also want to try a different time of day to make love. If you usually make love at night, try giving your lover a little morning surprise.

✦ 3. SPECIAL PREPARATION

When candles are lit, romantic music is played, silk sheets
are put onto the bed, and extraordinary care is given to the act of
making love, it sets the stage for a romantic pleasure. It does not have
to be candles and music, either; it may be leather and handcuffs.
Whatever turns you on! Just as long as the stage is set with mutual
passion and mutual consent.

One of the subtler approaches to setting the stage is the
massage. Dim the lights. Use hot (not too hot) oil and take the
time to focus on your partner's body. Concentrating on the
upper legs, lower abdomen, and the buttocks can be quite
arousing. Add candles and soft music to the scene and watch out!

✦ 4. SEX TOYS

The consensus is that sex toys can be titillating additions to
sensual pleasure, but that these devices are not essential to
sexual satisfaction. If you haven't tried any of these devices, it
is recommended that you and your partner experiment with them
and see how you like them. There is, in fact, a certain degree of
sexual excitement in just making the purchase, especially
if you do it together. (Expect to be a little nervous making your
first purchase.)

✦ 5. NEW POSITIONS

Lesbian couples stated that they are mostly satisfied with the
one or two positions which have become standard in their relationship, but that periodically they were excited by new positions introduced into their lovemaking.

Look over the five ideas listed above. Talk to your partner about the order of
preference you would each give them. There may be some surprises in store if both of
you are totally honest. If you and your partner have not had sex for a while, for whatever reason, and if you are both interested in reigniting the passion in your
relationship, you may want to keep in mind that the best way to revive your sex life is

to start having sex again. Sound simple? It is. All sex is good sex if it results in fun for both partners and in greater intimacy. Don't let other people's opinions dictate how often you *should* be having sex. Have it as often as you both want it. Try to make love when both of you are feeling energetic. At the end of a long workday is not always the best time to engage in sex. Also, try to be sexually appealing to your partner. You obviously were at one time. Don't let that disappear. Go to some trouble to make her do a double-take. Just because you feel secure with your relationship doesn't mean you should neglect your appearance. Be attractive for your woman. She's worth it!

Sex Is Not Everything, But It Sure Is Something!

If you haven't already established a situation in your relationship where you can talk to your partner openly about your sexual desires and needs, you need to do that right away. Seek lesbian-friendly professional help if you need assistance in this area; therapists can help you communicate more effectively with your partner. Because passion is such a great source of pleasure and intimacy, make sure to keep it alive in your relationship.

"The only sin passion can commit is to be joyless."
— Dorothy L. Sayers, writer

SEXUAL FANTASIES

Do you and your partner share sexual thoughts? Does it embarrass you to verbalize what goes on in your head? Do you feel depraved because you have sexual fantasies floating through your head at times? Do you feel cheated because you don't ever have sexual fantasies? Don't put too much pressure on yourself. Some people have fantasies all the time; others don't ever have them. No matter where you fall on the continuum — it's okay. But brace yourself — in the upcoming exercise, you're going to create a sexual fantasy. Even if you've never had a sexual fantasy before, you're going to hang loose and have one in a little while.

Exercise #32-A

Name_____

Separately from your partner, create a sexual fantasy that involves your partner.
Within your fantasy, respond to the following questions:

Where are you? What time of day is it? Is anyone else there?

What are each of you wearing (if anything)? What do you say to each other
(if anything)? How do you feel? What feeling do you get when you touch
your lover? Let your imagination frolic!

_____

_____

_____

_____

_____

_____

_____

_____

_____

_____

Exercise #32-B

Name_____

Separately from your partner, create a sexual fantasy that involves your partner. Within your fantasy, respond to the following questions:

Where are you? What time of day is it? Is anyone else there?

What are each of you wearing (if anything)? What do you say to each other (if anything)? How do you feel? What feeling do you get when you touch your lover? Let your imagination frolic!

_____

_____

_____

_____

_____

_____

_____

_____

After you have both completed Exercise #32, crawl into bed together and talk about your sexual fantasies. Have fun!

Small Acts of Love
Can Be Big Turn-ons!

Exercise #32-B

Name_____

Separately from your partner, create a sexual fantasy that involves your partner.
Within your fantasy, respond to the following questions:

Where are you? What time of day is it? Is anyone else there?

What are each of you wearing (if anything)? What do you say to each other
(if anything)? How do you feel? What feeling do you get when you touch
your lover? Let your imagination frolic!

_____

_____

_____

_____

_____

_____

_____

_____

After you have both completed Exercise #32, crawl into bed together and talk about
your sexual fantasies. Have fun!

Small Acts of Love
Can Be Big Turn-ons!

9

BESTOW APPRECIATION
UPON HER

Some of us prefer appreciation to be displayed in subtle ways, while others of us like it to be showered upon us like confetti in a parade. Whichever is your preference, the bottom line is that everyone wants to be appreciated, especially by that very special person with whom you share your life.

"Look at me! Look at me!"

When we were growing up, we needed our parents or other close relatives to make us feel worthwhile, important and valued. Remember when you were a kid and it was crucial for your mother to see you do a somersault fifty times or hear you sing a song or look at a painting or drawing that you had done? We needed the applause even if we didn't always get it. As we grew older, we then needed the applause from our friends. By the time we reached adulthood, we were mostly able to applaud ourselves for a job well done. Applauding ourselves is great, but it's still so much more rewarding when the applause comes from people we respect and admire. Your lover, whom you respect and admire, is a wonderful audience for your accomplishments today; and you, too, are a wonderful audience for her accomplishments. Don't assume that your partner knows she does a good job in various aspects of life. The little kid inside of you and the little kid inside of her still want the applause. Don't hold back on the adulation! Give it in large doses! Make it sincere! Giving the praise can be just as uplifting and satisfying as receiving it. Watch what happens when you do! Applauding your partner's successes or letting her know how much you love her and appreciate her can be incredibly contagious.

In fact, showing your appreciation for your partner is implicit in **all** of the topics discussed in *Feathering Your Nest*. You are saying that you appreciate this special person in your life by making an authentic commitment, by creating a home and family with this partner, by setting up goals and attaining them as a team, by communicating effectively and lovingly, by fighting honorably, by problem-solving in a positive way, by filling your life together with fun and excitement, by creating romance to keep the passion alive, by making sex a wonderful part of your intimate bond, and by allowing your partner to grow separately from yourself. It's important to let your lover know that you are truly grateful to have her in your life, that you believe that she is a great asset to your life, and that you admire her for being exactly who she is.

What Can Be More Uplifting Than Knowing You Are Truly Appreciated?

Celebrate your partner's successes. If she graduates from high school, college or a vocational program, celebrate it. If she gets her GED or makes an A on a test, celebrate it. If she receives a promotion or a raise at work, celebrate it. If she completes the triathlon or a 10K race for which she worked so hard, celebrate it. If she "comes out" to her parents and is happy with the end results, celebrate it. If she finally opens up that business that she's always wanted to open, celebrate it. Whatever your partner's successes are, let her know that you are proud of her. By doing this, your partner feels better about herself and about you. By the way, you shouldn't overlook your own successes. Celebrate it all. Heartfelt praise speaks love!

The Great Joy Of Life Is Knowing That We've Made A Positive Difference

In the following exercises, you and your partner will be given the opportunity to let each other know just how valuable you are to each other.

Exercise #33-A

Name_____

Separately from your lover, complete the following exercise. As you think about your partner, fill out the following sentences as honestly as possible.

1. I appreciate my partner most when she...

     a.

     b.

     c.

2. Name three physical traits that you love about your partner.

     a.

     b.

     c.

3. Name three personality traits that you love about your partner.

     a.

     b.

     c.

4. It amazes me how my partner...

     a.

     b.

     c.

5. I wish that my partner and I could...

     a.

     b.

     c.

6. When I see my partner across the room at a party, I feel...

     a.

     b.

     c.

7. I love my partner because she is...

     a.

     b.

     c.

8. I would like to thank my partner for...

     a.

     b.

9. For my partner, I am going to try to be more...

    a.

    b.

    c.

10. My partner is the World's Best...

    a.

    b.

    c.

Exercise #33-B

Name_____

Separately from your partner, complete the following exercise. As you think about your partner, fill in the following blanks as honestly as possible.

1. I appreciate my partner most when she...

    a.

    b.

    c.

2. Name three physical traits that you love about your partner.

    a.

    b.

    c.

3. Name three personality traits that you love about your partner.

    a.

    b.

    c.

4. It amazes me how my partner...

    a.

    b.

    c.

5. I wish that my partner and I could...

    a.

    b.

    c.

6. When I see my partner across the room at a party, I feel...

    a.

    b.

    c.

7. I love my partner because she is...

    a.

    b.

8. I would like to thank my partner for...

    a.

    b.

    c.

9. For my partner, I am going to try to be more...

    a.

    b.

    c.

10. My partner is the World's Best...

    a.

    b.

    c.

After each of you have completed the sentences in Exercise #33, make two copies of the exercise. Give one copy to your lover; in fact, you can create a special occasion in order to exchange copies in a romantic setting. Put the other copy in a safe place where you can frequently remind yourself of what a wonderful woman you have in your life. Tape it to the back of your closet door or to the side of your bookshelf. Wherever you decide to keep it, make sure it is someplace where you can daily remind yourself of how special this woman is.

Exercise #34

Let's recapture that artistic feeling we all had when we were in 2nd grade! Do this exercise when both you and your partner have about 45 - 60 minutes to play with each other like kids. You'll need the following equipment: 2 pairs of scissors; a glue stick, paste or tape; old newspapers and/or magazines; 2 pieces of construction paper or 2 pages of typing paper.

Here's what to do: Cut words and/or phrases out of the newspapers and/or magazines that represent your partner. You'll end up with a collage or, at least, a partial collage. Set the timer. When your time is up, present each other with your collages.

Many of you may be thinking that you'll pass on this activity. Don't! Once you start cutting out the first piece of your collage from the newspaper or magazine, you'll be glad you stayed with the activity! Be positive! Have fun!

"There is one happiness in life, to love and be loved."
— George Sand, writer

Showing your appreciation for your lover is a fairly simple act. During the courtship, you can bet there were lots of compliments and words of praise for each other. Is your partner just supposed to remember those wonderful experiences from the dating period? Is she supposed to assume you still feel the way you used to feel? One reason people often stray from their relationships is because a new person comes along and tells them things that make them feel loved, worthwhile and valued. This new person comes along and says all of the charming things that you said when you won your partner's heart in the first place. Loving thoughts expressed can be the most effective aphrodisiac and the sweetest essence of romance. Don't ever take your partner for granted. Never stop using phrases like "Thank you," "I love you," and "I'm sorry" with your partner. Use all three frequently and tenderly. It's important not to let your partner forget her worth in your life. You have to make sure the words and acts of appreciation remain a constant element in your relationship. **It matters!**

≈≈≈ 10 ≈≈≈

GROW SEPARATELY! GROW TOGETHER!

Although there is perhaps no one in the world with whom you'd rather spend your time, it is vital that you and your partner spend some time apart in order to nurture your individual growth; after all, you and your lover are two separate beings, not one. Encourage your partner to grow beyond where she is. Yes, separate and apart from you! Encourage your partner to go back to school, to take a new job, to learn a skill that interests her, to attend an out-of-town seminar, to spend time with her family and friends, to spend time alone, or to do whatever else she wants to do in order to enrich her life. Support her decision to learn new information and to encounter new experiences. Sometimes it feels threatening to let the woman you love go forward without you or in a different direction from you. The familiar is comfortable. You may feel that if your loved one wants to grow from where she is, she may be bored with you. In addition, you may feel that if you encourage her to grow, she may stray far from you and decide she wants to leave the relationship. There's no greater love than that which says, "Go on and grow even if this bond which I cherish is dissolved." If you feel threatened, perhaps it's time for a little self-esteem building on your own part. Keep in mind that the two of you are one family. Trust your partner. How do you want the inhabitants of your nest to be characterized? As two fulfilled and independent individuals loving the other in mutual respect, or as two unfulfilled and dependent leeches clinging to each other in desperation? In a healthy relationship, you will want your partner to be all she can possibly be. Besides, it's only when your lover is happy and fulfilled with herself that she can truly be happy and fulfilled with you. By the same token, we cannot promote another person's growth if we don't promote our own.

Exercise #35-A

Name_____

Separately from your partner, mark your response to each of the following statements using the scale provided.

> A - Always
> B - Often
> C - Sometimes
> D - Hardly ever
> E - Never

____ 1. When I want to try something new (e.g., college, new job, skill), my partner encourages me.

____ 2. When I make attempts to improve myself, my partner supports me.

____ 3. When I succeed in getting ahead on the job or in my education, my partner cheers me on.

____ 4. When I tell my partner that I need "alone" time, she reacts in an understanding manner.

____ 5. When I spend time with friends or family without my partner, I know that my relationship is still safe and secure.

It is when partners stifle each other's growth, when they feel they must share everything, when they feel they must stay within the other's grasp, that trouble starts to threaten the relationship. Neither of you needs to be leashed to the other in order to stay with each other. The paradox is this: Smothering and desperately grasping pushes away; encouraging and supporting unconditionally attracts toward.

Exercise #35-B

Name_____

Separately from your partner, mark your response to each of the following statements using the scale provided.

> A - Always
> B - Often
> C - Sometimes
> D - Hardly ever
> E - Never

____ 1. When I want to try something new (e.g., college, new job, skill), my partner encourages me.

____ 2. When I make attempts to improve myself, my partner supports me.

____ 3. When I succeed in getting ahead on the job or in my education, my partner cheers me on.

____ 4. When I tell my partner that I need "alone" time, she reacts in an understanding manner.

__ 5. When I spend time with friends or family without my partner, I know that my relationship is still safe and secure.

When you have both completed Exercise #35, join one another in a discussion of your answers. Hopefully most of your answers fell into the "A" or "B" ranking. If any of your answers fell into the "D" or "E" ranking, you may want to consider seeking professional help in order to resolve the insecurity issues.

GROW SEPARATELY

If you and your partner allow each other to develop separately from one another, you can come back together and share your growth. If either of you undermines or opposes the development of the other because of fear issues within yourself, expect resentment to eventually emerge.

When your lover shows an interest in something outside of you, don't take it as a personal assault. Comments like, "Why doesn't she want to spend time with me?" and, "I don't have to go outside our relationship to have fun" are not relevant. The point is that we are individuals, and while we get great pleasure from spending time with each other, it is important to develop outside interests to keep us brimming with inner vitality. It's what will keep you dazzled and intrigued! If the other areas of your relationship are in good working order, you don't need to fear losing your lover. If the other areas are not in good working order, get busy feathering your nest. In either case, attempts to stifle your partner's growth will certainly result in resentment.

Whatever your lover's interest, support it. If she wants to learn to play the guitar, give her time alone to practice and refrain from laughing when she plays "Smoke on the Water" or "Stairway to Heaven" or any songs that you should recognize but don't. If your lover wants to lose weight, help by buying and preparing foods that are low-fat and low in calories and/or exercise with her. Don't taunt your lover with fattening food when you know that her interest is in losing weight. Be supportive even though the interest area is outside you.

Although giving someone the space to explore and enjoy her own interests is commendable, actually contributing to her endeavor is better still. If your lover is a runner, for example, give her a warm foot bath and oil massage when she comes home from a run. If your lover is a teacher, set up some healthy snacks and tea and then help her grade the objective parts of student tests. If your lover has a high-stress job, play soft music and give her a shoulder massage in a candlelit room when she comes home. It doesn't matter what outside interests or occupation your partner has, you can help create an atmosphere to let her know that she is appreciated and loved for being the individual that she is.

There's No Warmer Feeling
Than Coming Home to a
Feathered Nest

The next set of exercises asks you to consider what it was that drew the two of you together in the first place. If you have been together for a very long time as a couple and can't quite remember how it all began, you may want to look through your early photographs and talk about the early days together in order to revive the spark.

Exercise #36-A

Name_____

Separately from your partner, answer the following two questions:

1. Name the #1 trait that initially attracted you to your partner.

2. Name the #1 trait that you believe initially attracted your partner to you.

Exercise #36-B

Name_____

Separately from your partner, answer the following two questions:

   1. Name the #1 trait that initially attracted you to your partner.

   2. Name the #1 trait that you believe initially attracted your partner to you.

After completing Exercise #36, discuss your answers together and revel in the memories.

Often what draws us to our partners are the differences; but whether the initial attractions were based on similarities or differences, you're here together now and you want to stay together. Consider both the similarities and the differences as assets to your relationship. Go from where you are and strengthen the bond between yourselves by expressing your appreciation. Make no mistake — she wants to know. One of the greatest expressions of appreciation is encouraging your partner to develop herself fully as an individual.

Comments: ✍

Exercise #37-A

Name_____

Separately from your partner, name two interest areas that you would like to see your partner develop more fully.

    1.

    2.

Name two interest areas that you would like to develop more fully for yourself.

    1.

    2.

Name two interest areas that you would like to develop **with** your partner.

    1.

    2.

Comments: ✍

Exercise #37-B

Name_____

Separately from your partner, name two interest areas that you would like to see your partner develop more fully.

    1.

    2.

Name two interest areas that you would like to develop more fully for yourself.

    1.

    2.

Name two interest areas that you would like to develop **with** your partner.

    1.

    2.

Comments:

Each of us has a wealth of information and interests that we sometimes keep to ourselves. Where each of you has your own interest, come together and share what the other might find stimulating. If you have a talent for playing a musical instrument or the ability to make pottery, for example, your partner might like to try her hand at it. Sharing our talents, skills, and/or knowledge could prove to be a pleasurable experience in your relationship. Remember that what comes easy to you, may not come easy to your partner, and vice versa; therefore, be patient and loving in your exchange. There is a need to nurture ourselves and to nurture our partners! Share your gifts.

GROW TOGETHER

Growing together as a couple is just as important as growing as individuals, for it strengthens the bond. While giving each other space to grow is important, it can also be fun and exciting to acquire certain knowledge or skills together. If you and your lover have an interest in learning a foreign language, for example, take a class together. To give you a special incentive for learning the language, plan a trip to a place where you'd need that language to communicate. If you would both like to learn to cook Honduran food, go to the library or bookstore to find cookbooks on the subject, go to a Central American grocery (if available in your area) and buy the necessary ingredients, and spend a free day in the kitchen cooking. You can do all of these activities while spending time together. The most rewarding activities are those that generate fun and promote learning. The list on the next page is limited, but it may give you and your partner some ideas of interest areas that you may want to pursue.

You Can Learn How To...

Place a check ✔ next to any activity that is appealing.

- ❏ draw, paint or sculpt
- ❏ sell real estate
- ❏ skydive or scuba dive
- ❏ sign language
- ❏ repair your car
- ❏ play bridge
- ❏ swim
- ❏ do yoga
- ❏ give CPR/first aid
- ❏ frame and mat pictures
- ❏ do your own taxes
- ❏ juggle
- ❏ do floral arranging
- ❏ bodybuild

- ❏ play a musical instrument
- ❏ give a massage
- ❏ build a deck or a piece of furniture
- ❏ repair small household appliances
- ❏ research your family trees
- ❏ cook (Thai, Mexican, low-fat, etc.)
- ❏ brew your own beer
- ❏ self defense (some martial art form)
- ❏ make jewelry
- ❏ develop your own photographs
- ❏ dance (ballroom, tap, country)
- ❏ speak more eloquently
- ❏ write short stories or poetry
- ❏ landscape your garden

For more information on other interest areas and on where you can go to learn what it is you want to learn, check with your local colleges/community colleges or with businesses that cater to these interests. Many lesbian and gay organizations in larger cities conduct classes in some of these areas. By the way, it's an excellent idea for **all** lesbians to be able to defend themselves; it's no secret that there are some unstable people out there who may try to harm others. Seriously consider some sort of self-defense class.

Exercise #38

Together, as a couple, list 3 interests you would like to pursue together.

1.

2.

3.

If attending classes doesn't appeal to you, take a look at the list below, which names types of worthwhile organizations and clubs that might provide you and your lover with fun and interesting diversions.

Together, You Can Join A...

Place a check ✔ next to any activity that is appealing.

❑ travel club   ❑ choral group

❑ museum   ❑ book club

❑ gym or health spa   ❑ local theater

❑ country club   ❑ bowling or tennis league

❑ activist/political organization   ❑ running or hiking club

❑ lesbian-friendly church/temple   ❑ softball/volleyball team

❑ playground coaching team   ❑ service organization to assist
       to help with little league   PWA or breast cancer patients

Exercise #39

Together, list three organizations and/or clubs that interest both of you.

     1.

     2.

     3.

Many lesbian and gay communities, again especially in larger cities, sponsor many of the types of activities listed on the previous page. Find out what they offer. Choose activities that you both enjoy.

Being Productively Active
Keeps Boredom Away.

Comments:

~ 11 ~

CREATE FUN AND EXCITEMENT

Very often, especially at the beginning of a relationship, couples will cut everybody off from their lives in order to focus completely on their new love; certainly this pattern is not limited just to lesbians. Then, after being in the relationship for a while, couples frequently begin to feel a bit disenchanted when their lives begin to lack some of the earlier fun and excitement that existed at the outset of the relationship. For a while they had assumed this new love would fulfill all their needs. What a burden to put on the woman you love!

Involving yourselves in outside activities and interests, like the ones discussed in Chapter 10, is a good way to relieve some of that burden and that boredom. Another way is to develop a network of friends, especially other couples, to bring new thoughts and energy to your relationship. While it is important to have a sense of your "community," a sisterhood of lesbians, you may want to consider widening your circle to include others. Many lesbians limit their friendships solely to the lesbian community. While there is certainly some great company there, you are depriving yourself of a world of diversity. When you select your friends, you may want to ask yourself this key question:

Does This Person Enrich My Life?

Wherever you can find positive people who contribute to your well-being, welcome them into your lives and cherish them. A person's gender, sexual preference, age, color, religion, etc., are all really quite irrelevant. It's a pretty safe bet that if you surround yourself with people who are vital and genuinely happy with themselves, you'll be surrounding yourself with people who will enrich and illuminate your life.

When Things Get Dull...

There are very few of us who live lives filled with constant fun and excitement. Is the following scenario a familiar one?

> A couple is sitting on the sofa with the television set on. Bored with sitting in front of the box, one of them asks her partner, "What do you want to do?" Her partner responds, "I don't know. What do you want to do?" The first one declares, "I don't know, but I do know that I don't want to watch TV." The second one replies, "Me either. What do you want to do?" The couple remains on the sofa staring at the television.

Television is not the only option in life. Unfortunately, many people have gotten into the rut of depending on it to provide all of their entertainment. Some are quite satisfied with sitting there; others are not. If you are not, **Get Up and Play!**

Throughout this chapter, you will be provided with lists of activities that you and your partner may enjoy. Some are activities that you'll just want to share with one another; the others are activities for you and your circle of friends.

It's important for couples not to spend all of their recreational time in the lesbian bars, or any other bar for that matter. Some lesbians see the bar as a type of home away from home. Although lesbian bars do serve an important social function in the community, there are so many other wonderful ways to spend your leisure time that it's no longer the only way to meet other women and have fun. Why not become involved in other aspects of your community's life?

Fun Activities to Enjoy With Other Couples

1. Form a dinner club consisting of from one to several other couples. Dine together either once a week, once a month, or whenever your group decides. The dinners — whether gourmet or simple home cooking — can either be held by a different couple each time, or can be potluck dinners arranged by all involved.

2. Join a sports league (e.g., golf, bowling, softball, volleyball) or start one. You don't have to be superjocks; you can do it for the fun of it. It doesn't hurt that this type of activity helps keep you in good shape. If you don't want to be committed to a team that meets on a regular basis, get a group of friends together for the day to play ball or go bowling.

3. Form a walking group and meet 3-4 times a week in the park to walk. You might want to follow it up with a visit to the coffee shop or to one of your homes.

4. Poker or Bridge Night. Any type of card game will do.

5. Board Game Night. There are many entertaining board games that can produce lots of laughs and fun for a group of 4 or more.

6. Beer tastings. Each couple or person (if you're not dealing with couples only) brings a six-pack of unusual beers. Unusual beers would be those you don't commonly see on the market shelves. They might include beers from Africa, Japan, Honduras, etc., or from one of many micro-breweries. You may want one or two people to bring crackers to cleanse the palette between the different beers.

7. Wine tasting (same as #6 but with wine).

8. Have a picnic and invite the couples who have children or nieces and nephews to bring them along. Make sure you have some fun activities planned for the kids (e.g., softball, pantomime, badminton).

9. Plan a weekend away with friends. Rent a cabin big enough for 2-3 couples. Invite other couples to rent nearby cabins. Plan (but don't overplan) certain activities; for example, you might plan an Italian Night where you'd play Italian music, serve Chianti and a spaghetti dish, and decorate with red-and-white checkered tablecloths. Other great themes for parties might include Western Night, Hippie Party, 50's Party, Famous People Party, Cross Dress Party, Come-Dressed-As-Your-Partner Party, Gangster Night, etc.

10. Plan a trip through a travel agency that offers cruises and other outings for lesbians only. There really are travel agencies like this. Peruse any local lesbian/gay newspaper or magazine. If you have no luck there, ask any of the lesbian/gay establishments in your area to help you find more information. Usually these establishments are happy to help.

11. With some friends, charter a fishing boat for the day or for half a day. Chartered boats often provide all of the fishing equipment, bait, ice, etc. There are some boats that will take as few as 8-12 people out at a time.

12. Throw a dance party at your house. Invite 2-3 other couples. Dim the lights and put a great dance tape on the cassette player. You can, if you wish, make this activity a theme party.

13. Form a literary circle. After deciding on a novel to read, come together after a week or two and discuss the book. If reading is not your thing, you can do the same thing with movies.

14. Get your musically talented friends together and have an informal jam session. Try to get everyone involved, even if it entails having someone keep the beat on the bottom of a cooking pot.

15. Have a slumber party at which two or three other couples come over and stay up all night talking and laughing together.

16. With your friends, brainstorm more activities for lesbian couples.

The Number of Activities is Infinite!

Many of the activities we described can be combined with other activities. For example, if you plan on a evening of playing board games, you can have a halftime activity that includes the wine-tasting or beer-tasting activity. You can also do personal-preference alterations on the activities listed; for example, if you and your lover do not drink alcohol, you can have couples bring recipes for the most delicious nonalcoholic beverage and have a tasting of those drinks.

Exercise #40

Lesbians are a pretty creative breed. Think of five more activities to add to the list of activities for couples. If you think of more, list them in the margin or in the "Personal Notes" section at the back of the book.

1.

2.

3.

4.

5.

Couples need to play not only with other couples but also with each other. Often at the beginning of a romantic relationship, couples are playful with each other; but as the day-to-day grind once more resurfaces, they sometimes forget how to play. In case you've forgotten, you need to relearn the art. Life beyond the nest can sometimes be hectic and burdensome. If you and your partner create fun between you, you can alleviate much of that stress.

Never Say There's Nothing to Do!

Below you will find a list of 33 activities. These are just a few of an endless number of ideas! When you and your lover are at a standstill about what to do, check out the list.

❐ Get a license and go fishing

❐ Buy canvas and some acrylic paints and paint an abstract

❐ Go horseback riding

❐ Go bowling

❐ Landscape the yard together

❐ Go to the zoo, aquarium or museum

❐ Groom the dog together

❐ Paint a room of your house

❐ Invite friends or family over

❐ Rent a canoe at a nearby park

❐ Go to a nearby ballpark and watch a game in progress

❐ Lie in bed and tell funny stories about your childhood

❐ Take a sight-seeing tour of your own town

❐ Cook an exotic meal

❐ Go to a local play or poetry reading

❐ Go to a rodeo

❐ Go roller-skating or ice-skating

❐ Hang out in a music store that lets you listen to different CDs on headphones

❐ Pack an ice chest and food basket and take a road trip

❐ Split a banana split or sundae

❐ Rent a gay or lesbian movie, like *Desert Hearts* or *Go Fish*

❐ Listen to a movie soundtrack of *Evita* or *Les Miserables*, and sing along

❐ Go dancing

❐ Visit a fun friend or relative

❐ Dig out an old photo album and reminisce about shared fun times

❐ Give each other facials

❐ Plan a trip together by bike or auto

❐ Go to the mall or some other shopping area

❐ Meet your neighbors

❐ Play pool

❐ Play hopscotch, jump rope, or other games you played as a kid

❐ Paint each other's toenails in bed

❐ Take a nap near a stream or lake

❐ Invite friends over for a "come as your partner" party

❐ Go antique hunting

❐ Go to a local auction

Make a date with your partner. Ask her out for a specific night. Plan the evening on your own and then surprise her with a splendid night out where you focus all of your attention on her. Go to some trouble dressing up for her. Don't make mention of how much the evening is costing (not that it has to be expensive) and don't allow any problems to crop up for discussion. Just focus on your partner. Make her laugh. Make her glad to be with you. Let her know that she is still your sweetheart and that you still adore her.

Don't Ever Stop Dating Your Partner

Check your local entertainment guide, your local newspaper or on-line computer listings for fun happenings (e.g., festivals, fairs, musical events) in your area. Keep a drawer or a special place in your home for flyers advertising upcoming events, ads for cheap travel packages or upcoming concerts, entertainment and restaurant guides, and, of course, refer to *Feathering Your Nest* whenever you need to. Know that you can just run to this special place and immediately find myriad fun activities to share.

There's a world of pleasure and adventure out there! Don't get glued to the television set or stuck upon a bar stool. Many of the activities are to be enjoyed by just you and your lover; others can be enjoyed with another individual or with other couples.

Exercise #41

Together, add five more activities that you and your lover might enjoy alone.

    1.

    2.

    3.

    4.

    5.

Learn to play with your partner. Remember: She is your best friend! Plan for fun! Buy season tickets to concerts or plays being performed at a nearby university. Be spontaneous about fun! Jump in the car and go road tripping. Whatever you do, make sure the two of you have fun times together. When you laugh together, it keeps your relationship healthy, intimate and exciting. When you and your partner are together, you should do all you can to relieve yourselves of the pressures from the outside world. You can be a delightful refuge for each other.

"Laughter is by definition healthy."

— Doris Lessing

Exercise #42

Together, list three of the funniest experiences you have shared as a couple. Think of experiences where the two of you just couldn't stop laughing. (If you have problems coming up with this list, let it incubate and come back to it later.)

1.

2.

3.

Once you start focusing on the funniest experiences you've shared, you shouldn't be surprised by the resulting laughter. You may even find that you laugh harder now than when the incidents originally occurred. If once you start talking about these experiences, you come up with more than three, please scribble in the additional episodes in the margins or in the "Personal Notes" section at the back of the book. Add to the list as you encounter more amusing experiences. Can you imagine ever having too many laughs or too much humor in your relationship?

Not only is it healthy to laugh as a couple, you should also be able to laugh at yourself. Have you ever gotten exasperated over something that was quite trivial and undeserving of your aggravation? Have you ever gotten upset because you misconstrued something you thought your lover was saying that turned out to be innocent enough? Be able to laugh at your mistakes, at your misunderstandings, at yourself; at the same time, be loving and appreciative of the wonderful person that you are.

Because you and your lover are in a safe place together, grant yourselves permission to be silly and carefree at times. Samba in the kitchen even if you don't know the first thing about doing the samba. Make up songs and sing them to each other. It doesn't matter how ridiculous the lyrics are; in fact, the more ridiculous, the better. When you have the opportunity, enjoy each other. If the opportunity doesn't present itself, create it.

Creating fun and excitement within your relationship doesn't always entail setting off the proverbial fireworks. Cuddling and talking in bed, leaning back against a tree reading a book, or holding hands and staring up at the stars can be just as fun and exciting. The point, which has been made in each chapter of *Feathering Your Nest,* is to create a place where you both want to be in life.

CONCLUSION:

Work At Making
It Work

Feathering Your Nest is intended to go beyond skimming the surface of relationships. It is about helping you feel secure and safe in the knowledge that each of you will stay around to work out the inevitable conflicts. It is also about creating an exciting and fulfilling life with the woman you love. Not only is it a dream that many lesbians want to achieve in order to lead happier and healthier lives, it is a dream that all lesbians **can** achieve.

Whatever barriers you face in your relationship, you have the power to surmount them. As a couple, it is important for you and your partner to focus on the areas listed below.

1. Developing your own family with its own special traditions
2. Creating a fun and goal-oriented relationship
3. Keeping the romance alive and the sex pleasurable
4. Maintaining open and respectful communication in all areas of your lives together — problem-solving, arguing, and expressing feelings and thoughts in general
5. Continuing to grow as individuals as well as a couple
6. Respecting and trusting your partner while learning to appreciate the differences between you
7. Showing your appreciation for the woman with whom you have chosen to share your life

About the Authors

Gwen Leonhard has taught literature and composition in a metropolitan New Orleans public high school over a span of twenty years, and has blissfully been teaching the academically gifted for the past five years. She is also founder of the Positive Living Alliance (PLA), a personal improvement organization that combines the expertise of both the social work and educational fields in self growth workshops. Her undergraduate and graduate degrees in English and Education were attained from the University of New Orleans.

Jennie Mast, MSW, is a board certified social worker who is currently employed as a health care coordinator at Northshore Psychiatric Hospital. She attained her masters in social work at Tulane University, and her undergraduate degree in psychology and sociology at the University of New Orleans. Jennie has worked with Gwen Leonhard in the Positive Living Alliance for several years.

ANY ADDITIONAL SUGGESTIONS?
ANY QUESTIONS?
ANY INPUT AT ALL?

WE WANT TO HEAR FROM YOU!

———————————————

Your ideas may be used to create a *Feathering Your Nest*, Part II
to further assist lesbians
in developing more loving and fulfilling long-term relationships.

———————————————

If you have any feedback for the authors
of *Feathering Your Nest*, please contact
Gwen Leonhard
c/o Rising Tide Press
5 Kivy Street
Huntington Station, NY 11746

OTHER BOOKS OF INTEREST

❑ **NOW THAT YOU KNOW: What Every parent Should Know About Homosexuality**
Betty Fairchild & Nancy Hayward $9.95
One of the best books for parents about themselves in relation to their lesbian daughters and gay sons.
After reading it, many parents respond warmly & supportively to their children.

❑ **GAYELLOW PAGES: The National Edition**
Renaissance House $11.95
A reliable, newly revised guide which lists gay/lesbian resources in your community, state, and nation-wide: interest groups, restaurants, hotels/motels, publications, etc.

❑ **A LEGAL GUIDE FOR LESBIAN AND GAY COUPLES**
Curry, Clifford & Leonard $24.95
Covers all aspects of living together: forms & agreements to handle most legal situations: buying & selling property, child custody, living together arrangements, power of attorney, etc.

❑ **POSITIVELY GAY**
Betty Berzon $12.95
An affirmative book which helps overcome internalized homophobia so that we can accept ourselves and our lives positively.

HOW TO ORDER

Please send me the books I have checked. I enclose a check or money order (not cash), plus $3 for the first book and $1 for each additional book to cover shipping/handling. Or bill my ❑Visa/MC ❑Amex
Or call our Toll Free Number 1-800-648-5333 if using a credit card.

CARD # _____ EXP. DATE_____

SIGNATURE_____

NAME (PLEASE PRINT) _____

ADDRESS _____

CITY_____ STATE_____ ZIP_____
❑ New York State residents add 8.5% tax to total.

RISING TIDE PRESS
5 KIVY ST., HUNTINGTON STATION, NY 11746

Lesbian Fiction to Stir the Imagination from Rising Tide Press

RETURN TO ISIS
Jean Stewart
It is the year 2093, and Whit, a bold woman warrior from an Amazon nation, rescues Amelia from a dismal world where females are either breeders or drones. During their arduous journey back to the shining all-women's world of Artemis, they are unexpectedly drawn to each other. This engaging first book in the trilogy has it all—romance, mystery, and adventure.
Lambda Literary Award Finalist
ISBN 0-9628938-6-2; 192 Pages; $9.99

ISIS RISING
Jean Stewart
In this stirring romantic fantasy, the familiar cast of lovable characters begin to rebuild the colony of Isis, burned to the ground ten years earlier by the dread Regulators. But evil forces threaten to destroy their dream. A swashbuckling futuristic adventure and an endearing love story all rolled into one.
ISBN 0-9628938-8-9; 192 Pages; $11.99

WARRIORS OF ISIS
Jean Stewart
At last, the third lusty tale of high adventure and passionate romance among the Freeland Warriors. Arinna Sojourner, the evil product of genetic engineering, vows to destroy the fledgling colony of Isis with her incredible psychic powers. Whit, Kali, and other warriors battle to save their world, in this novel bursting with life, love, heroines and villains.
Lambda Literary Award Finalist
ISBN 1-883061-03-2; 256 Pages; $11.99

HEARTSTONE AND SABER
Jacqui Singleton
You can almost hear the sabers clash in this rousing tale of good and evil, of passionate love, of warrior queens and white witches. Cydell, the imperious queen of Mauldar, and Elayna, the Fair Witch of Avoreed, join forces to combat the evil that menaces the empire, and in the course of doing that, find rapturous love.
ISBN 1-883061-00-8; 224 Pages; $10.99

More Lesbian Fiction from Rising Tide Press

ROUGH JUSTICE
Claire Youmans

When Glenn Lowry's sunken fishing boat turns up four years after his disappearance, foul play is suspected. Classy, ambitious Prosecutor Janet Schilling immediately launches a murder investigation which produces several surprising suspects—one of them her own former lover Catherine Adams, now living a reclusive life in a lighthouse on Seal Rock Island. A fascinating page-turner. Filled with the beauty and danger of the sea and unexpected plot twists, *Rough Justice* poses an intriguing question: Is murder ever justified?
ISBN 1-883061-10-5; $10.99

NO WITNESSES
Nancy Sanra

This cliff-hanger of a mystery set in San Francisco, introduces Detective Tally McGinnis, the brains and brawn behind the Phoenix Detective Agency. When her ex-lover Pamela Tresdale is arrested for the grisly murder of a wealthy Texas heiress, Tally rushes to the rescue. Despite friends' warnings, Tally is drawn once again into Pamela's web of deception and betrayal, as she attempts to clear her and find the real killer. A gripping whodunit.
ISBN 1-883061-05-9; 192 Pages; $9.99

DANGER IN HIGH PLACES: An Alix Nicholson Mystery
Sharon Gilligan

Set against the backdrop of Washington, D.C., this riveting mystery introduces freelance photographer and amateur sleuth, Alix Nicholson. Alix stumbles on a deadly scheme surrounding AIDS funding, and with the help of a lesbian congressional aide, unravels the mystery.
ISBN 0-9628938-7-0; 176 Pages, $9.99

DANGER! CROSS CURRENTS: An Alix Nicholson Mystery
Sharon Gilligan

The exciting sequel to *Danger in High Places* brings freelance photographer Alix Nicholson face-to-face with an old love and a murder. When Alix's landlady, a real estate developer, turns up dead, and her much younger lover, Leah Claire, is the prime suspect, Alix launches a frantic campaign to find the real killer. ISBN 1-883061-01-6; 192 Pages; $9.99

More Lesbian Fiction
from Rising Tide Press

DEADLY RENDEZVOUS: A Toni Underwood Mystery
Diane Davidson
A string of brutal murders in the middle of the desert plunges Lieutenant Toni Underwood and her lover Megan into a high profile investigation which uncovers a world of drugs, corruption and murder, as well as the dark side of the human mind. An explosive, fast-paced, action-packed whodunit.
ISBN 1-883061-02-4; 224 pages; $9.99

DEADLY GAMBLE: A Toni Underwood Mystery
Diane Davidson
Retired detective Toni Underwood is catapulted back into the world of crime by a mysterious letter from her favorite aunt. The black sheep of the family because she is a prominent Las Vegas Madam, Aunt Vera fears she is about to be murdered—a distinct possibility given her underworld connections. Toni springs into action, enlists the help of former partner Sergeant Sally Murphy, and together, they take on the seamy, dangerous, razzle-dazzle of Las Vegas. A cast of flamboyant, unsavory characters and thugs makes for likely suspects, but as in *Deadly Rendezvous*, you'll never guess the ending. (Available 1/97)
ISBN 1-883061-12-1; $11.99

CORNERS OF THE HEART
Leslie Grey
A captivating novel of love and suspense in which beautiful French-born Chris Benet and English professor Katya Michaels meet and fall in love. But their budding love is shadowed by a vicious killer, whom they must outwit. Your heart will pound as the story races to its heart-stopping conclusion.
ISBN 0-9628938-3-8; 224 pages; $9.95

SHADOWS AFTER DARK
Ouida Crozier
When wings of death spread over Kyril's home world, she is sent to Earth on a mission—find a cure for the deadly disease. Once here she meets and falls in love with Kathryn, who is enthralled yet horrified to learn that her mysterious, darkly exotic lover is a vampire. This tender, beautifully written love story is the ultimate lesbian vampire novel!
ISBN 1-883061-50-4; 224 Pages; $9.95

EDGE OF PASSION
Shelley Smith
This sizzling novel about an all-consuming love affair between a younger and an older woman is set in colorful Provincetown. A gripping love story, which is both fierce and tender, it will keep you breathless until the last page.
ISBN 0-9628938-1-1; 192 Pages; $8.95

YOU LIGHT THE FIRE
Kristen Garrett
Here's a grown-up **Rubyfruit Jungle**—sexy, spicy, and sidesplittingly funny. Take a gorgeous, sexy, high school math teacher and put her together with a raunchy, commitment-shy, ex-rock singer, and you've got a hilarious, unforgettable love story.
ISBN 0-9628938-5-4; $9.95

EMERALD CITY BLUES
Jean Stewart
When the comfortable yuppie world of Chris Olson and Jennifer Hart collides with the desperate lives of Reb and Flynn, two lesbian runaways struggling to survive on the streets of Seattle, the forecast is trouble. A warmhearted, gritty, enormously readable novel of contemporary lesbigay life which raises real questions about the meaning of family and community, and about the walls we construct around our hearts. Finally, *Emerald City Blues* is a celebration of the healing powers of love. ISBN 1-883061-09-1; $11.99

PLAYING FOR KEEPS
Stevie Rios
In this sparkling tale of love and adventure, Lindsay West, an oboist, travels to Caracas, where she meets three people who change her life forever: Rob Heron a gay man, who becomes her dearest friend; Her lover Mercedes Luego, a lovely cellist, who takes Lindsay on a life-altering adventure down the Amazon; And the mysterious jungle-dwelling woman Arminta, who touches their souls. ISBN 1-883061-07-5; $10.99

DREAMCATCHER
Lori Byrd
This timeless story of love and friendship illuminates a year in the life of Sunny Calhoun, a college student, who falls in love with Eve Phillips, a literary agent. A richly woven narrative which captures the wonder and pain of love between a younger and an older woman—a woman facing AIDS with spirited courage and humor.
ISBN 1-883061-06-7; 192 Pp; $9.99

LOVESPELL
Karen Williams
A deliciously erotic and humorous love story in which Kate Gallagher, a shy veterinarian, and Allegra, who has magic at her fingertips, fall in love. A masterful blend of fantasy and reality, this beautifully written story will warm and delight your heart. ISBN 0-9628938-2-X; $9.95

NIGHTSHADE
Karen Williams
After witnessing a fateful hit-and-run accident, Alex Spherris finds herself the new owner of a magical bell, which some people would kill for. She is ushered into a strange fantasy world and meets Orielle, who melts her frozen heart. Don't miss this delightfully imaginative romance spun in the best tradition of storytelling. ISBN 1-883061-08-3; $11.99

FEATHERING YOUR NEST:
An Interactive Workbook & Guide to a Loving Lesbian Relationship
Gwen Leonhard, M.ED. & Jennie Mast, MSW
A fresh, insightful guide providing lesbian couples with effective ways to build and nourish their relationships. Bursting with creative ways to: build trust; solve conflict and fight fair; put spark in your sex life; conquer boredom, & enjoy life together. ISBN 1-883061-13-X; $14.99

SWEET BITTER LOVE
Rita Schiano
Susan Fredrickson is a woman of fire and ice—a successful high-powered executive, she is by turns sexy and aloof. And from the moment writer Jenny Ceretti spots her at the Village Coffeehouse, her serene life begins to change. As their friendship explodes into a blazing love affair, Jenny discovers that all is not as it appears, while Susan is haunted by ghosts from a past that won't stay hidden. Schiano serves up passion, courage, and clear-eyed honesty in this dramatic debut novel. A roller-coaster romance which vividly captures the rhythm and feel of love's sometimes rocky ride. ISBN 1-883061-15-6; 192 pages; $10.99

TROPICAL STORM
Linda Kay Silva
Another winning action-packed adventure/romance featuring smart and sassy heroines, an exotic rainforest setting, and a plot with more twists and turns than a coiled cobra. In this 5th book of the bestselling Storm series, Megan has disappeared into the Costa Rican rainforest and it's up to Delta and Connie to find her. Out of their element, with few clues to go on, they must battle an unfamiliar terrain —deadly jungle beasts, Colombian drug runners, and vicious slavers. Will Delta risk all for the woman she loves? ISBN 1-883061-14-8; $11.99; Avail. 1/97

HOW TO ORDER

TITLE   **AUTHOR**   **PRICE**

- ❑ **Corners of the Heart**-Leslie Grey 9.95
- ❑ **Danger! Cross Currents**-Sharon Gilligan 9.99
- ❑ **Danger in High Places**-Sharon Gilligan 9.95
- ❑ **Deadly Gamble**-Diane Davidson 11.99
- ❑ **Deadly Rendezvous**-Diane Davidson 9.99
- ❑ **Dreamcatcher**-Lori Byrd 9.99
- ❑ **Edge of Passion**-Shelley Smith 9.95
- ❑ **Emerald City Blues**-Jean Stewart 11.99
- ❑ **Feathering Your Nest**-Gwen Leonhard/ Jennie Mast 14.99
- ❑ **Heartstone and Saber**-Jacqui Singleton 10.99
- ❑ **Isis Rising**-Jean Stewart 11.99
- ❑ **Love Spell**-Karen Williams 9.99
- ❑ **Nightshade**-Karen Williams 11.99
- ❑ **No Witnesses**-Nancy Sanra 9.99
- ❑ **Playing for Keeps**-Stevie Rios 10.99
- ❑ **Return to Isis**-Jean Stewart 9.99
- ❑ **Rough Justice**-Claire Youmans 10.99
- ❑ **Shadows After Dark**-Ouida Crozier 9.99
- ❑ **Sweet Bitter Love**-Rita Schiano 10.99
- ❑ **Tropical Storm**-Linda Kay Silva 11.99
- ❑ **Warriors of Isis**-Jean Stewart 11.99
- ❑ **You Light the Fire**-Kristen Garrett 9.95

Please send me the books I have checked. I enclose a check or money order (not cash), plus $3 for the first book and $1 for each additional book to cover shipping and handling. Or bill my ❑Visa/MC ❑Amex.

Or call our Toll Free Number 1-800-648-5333 if using a credit card.

CARD # _____ EXP. DATE _____

SIGNATURE_____

NAME (PLEASE PRINT) _____

ADDRESS _____

CITY_____ STATE_____ ZIP_____

❑ New York State residents add 8.5% tax to total.

RISING TIDE PRESS

5 KIVY ST., HUNTINGTON STATION, NY 11746

Personal Notes

GWEN LEONHARD AND JENNIE MAST

Personal Notes

Personal Notes

Appendix A

Ways in which I want my lover to be romantic that I've never told her:

Partner A:_____

1. _____

2. _____

3. _____

4. _____

5. _____

Appendix B

Ways in which I want my lover to be romantic that I've never told her:

Partner B:_____

1. _____

2. _____

3. _____

4. _____

5. _____

Appendix C

Keeping Track Of Arguments

Partner A: _____

Date: _____

General Type of Argument:

_____

_____

Rules of honorable fighting used:

_____

_____

How was this argument resolved?

_____

_____

Appendix D

Keeping Track Of Arguments

Partner B: _____

Date: _____

General Type of Argument:

_____

_____

Rules of honorable fighting used:

_____

_____

How was this argument resolved?

_____

_____

Appendix E

Nagging Behaviors

Partner A: _____

Week of: _____

1. _____

2. _____

3. _____

4. _____

5. _____

6. _____

7. _____

8. _____

We Aren't Perfect Yet!

Appendix F

Nagging Behaviors

Partner B:_____

Week of: _____

1. _____

2. _____

3. _____

4. _____

5. _____

6. _____

7. _____

8. _____

We Aren't Perfect Yet!